QUICK MENTAL MATHS

MENTAL RECALL PRACTICE FOR 11 YEAR OLDS

SCHOLASTIC MATHS SKILLS

AUTHOR
William Hartley

EDITOR
Kate Pearce

ASSISTANT EDITOR
Claire Miller

SERIES DESIGNER
Anna Oliwa

DESIGNER
Sarah Rock

ILLUSTRATIONS
Nick Diggory

COVER ARTWORK
James Alexander/
David Oliver
(Berkeley
Studios)

Text © 1999 William Hartley
© 1999 Scholastic Ltd

Designed using Adobe Pagemaker
Published by Scholastic Ltd, Villiers House, Clarendon
Avenue, Leamington Spa, Warwickshire CV32 5PR

1234567890   9012345678

British Library Cataloguing-in-Publication Data
A catalogue record for this book is available from the
British Library.

ISBN 0-590-53923-X

SEC	SHEET	SHEET HEADING	SUGGESTED ORAL MATHS INPUT
COUNTING AND ORDERING	A1	COUNTING IN STEPS (INC NEGATIVE NUMBERS)	Count on/back in steps of any size.
	A2	PLACE VALUE	Practise place value with any size of number. See B11 and C11.
	A3	ORDERING WHOLE, FRACTIONAL AND % AMOUNTS	Order/compare whole, fractional, decimal & % amounts.
	A4	ESTIMATING AND APPROXIMATING	Estimate various quantities of any size of number.
	A5	ROUNDING WHOLE NUMBERS AND DECIMALS	Rounding any number to the nearest $\frac{1}{10}$ /10/100/1000.
	A6	TEST YOUR SKILLS 1 (A1–A3 REVIEW SHEET)	As for A1–A3.
	A7	TEST YOUR SKILLS 2 (A4–A5 REVIEW SHEET)	As for A4 and A5.
ADDITION AND SUBTRACTION	B1	ADDITION FACTS	Practise number pairs that total 100 or above.
	B2	SUBTRACTION FACTS	Facts for numbers up to 20 and multiples of 10/100/1000.
	B3	RELATIONSHIP BETWEEN + AND –	362 + 137 = 499. What are the three other related facts?
	B4	PAIRS AND DOUBLES	Practice doubles of whole numbers from 1 to 50 or more.
	B5	ADDING ORDER	Several numbers (some bridging). Start with the largest.
	B6	IDENTIFYING NEAR DOUBLES AND TREBLES	Problems like: 7000 + 6000 = double 7000 - 1000.
	B7	CALCULATION PATTERNS (+ AND –)	Problems like: 490 + 490, 480 + 500, 470 + 510, and so on.
	B8	PARTITIONING AND RECOMBINING	Partition into THTU and add the 1000s first.
	B9	BRIDGING AND ADJUSTING	eg, 384 + 285 = 384 + 300 – 15 = 684 – 15 = 669.
	B10	+/– WHOLE, FRACTIONAL, DECIMAL & % AMOUNTS	+ and – whole, fractional, decimal and % amounts.
	B11	PLACE VALUE WHEN ADDING AND SUBTRACTING	+ and – whole numbers and decimals. See A2 and C11.
	B12	ADDING AND SUBTRACTING SEVERAL NUMBERS	+ and – several two digit numbers with bridging.
	B13	TEST YOUR SKILLS 1 (B1–B6 REVIEW SHEET)	As for B1–B6.
	B14	TEST YOUR SKILLS 2 (B7–B12 REVIEW SHEET)	As for B7–B12.
MULTIPLICATION AND DIVISION	C1	MULTIPLICATION FACTS	Multiplication facts up to and beyond 10 × 10.
	C2	DIVISION FACTS	Division facts up to and beyond 100 ÷ 10.
	C3	RELATIONSHIP BETWEEN × AND ÷	Practise breaking numbers into sub-sets (× and ÷).
	C4	DOUBLES, TREBLES AND FRACTIONAL AMOUNTS	Practise ways of finding different fractional amounts.
	C5	PARTITIONING WHEN MULTIPLYING	Multiplying 100s first when multiplying HTU by U.
	C6	DIVISION WITH REMAINDERS	Divide THTU by 2 to 10. Alter remainders into fractions.
	C7	CALCULATION PATTERNS (× AND ÷)	Look for × and ÷ patterns in the 2 to 10 times tables.
	C8	FACTORS AND MULTIPLYING BY 10, 100, 1000	Factor games and decimal place shifting activities.
	C9	DIVIDING BY 10, 100, 1000	Division questions that involve decimal place shifting.
	C10	USING RELATED × AND ÷ FACTS	Give four facts for the numbers 70, 80 and 560.
	C11	PLACE VALUE WHEN MULTIPLYING AND DIVIDING	THTU problems. × and ÷ to 3 decimal places. See A2 and B11.
	C12	×/÷ WHOLE, FRACTIONAL, DECIMAL & % AMOUNTS	Practise ×/÷ facts for tables 2–10. ×/÷ fractions/decimals.
	C13	TEST YOUR SKILLS 1 (C1–C6 REVIEW SHEET)	As for C1–C6.
	C14	TEST YOUR SKILLS 2 (C7–C12 REVIEW SHEET)	As for C7–C12.
MULTISTEP AND MIXED OPERATIONS	D1	THE FOUR RULES OF NUMBER	Choose any relevant activity.
	D2	THE FOUR RULES OF NUMBER	Choose any relevant activity.
	D3	THE FOUR RULES OF NUMBER	Choose any relevant activity.
	D4	THE FOUR RULES OF NUMBER	Choose any relevant activity.

ABOUT THE SERIES

Quick Mental Maths aims to help children develop quick mental recall strategies – both the instant recall of known facts and speedy methods of figuring out 'unknowns'. Number facts are the vital building blocks for calculation, and their easy access is the key to efficient, accurate and confident mental mathematical ability.

Quick Mental Maths is a series of six photocopiable books providing a mixture of problem-posing styles of mental number practice for children aged 6 to 11. The level of ability at which each book is pitched has been broadly determined from the recommendations of the National Numeracy *Framework* document. *Quick Mental Maths* can be used as an independent resource in its own right to support any of the UK curriculum documentation, but can also be used in conjunction with the other Scholastic series *Developing Mental Maths* and *Practising Mental Maths*.

The books will provide valuable reinforcement of number bonds and times tables and help to improve the children's mental agility, as well as consolidating and extending their knowledge and use of mathematical vocabulary. These worksheets could be used as regular number practice – perhaps with a short time allowed each day for the children to complete one or more sections of a worksheet – as pre-SATs reinforcement/assessment tasks, or as worthwhile homework pages. All photocopiable sheets are indicated by the icon 🅿.

ABOUT THE BOOK STRUCTURE
IN-BUILT DIFFERENTIATION

Each of the six books in this series addresses the same mental maths content under the same worksheet heading in each book, but at an increasing level of complexity. Thus, for example, you will find that worksheet A2 is always 'Place value' and worksheet C6 is always about 'Division with remainders'. Therefore, differentiation in a mixed-ability class is made easy by using the same worksheet number from more than one book to provide the same material at different levels.

YOUR INPUT

In order to reinforce the intended strategy to be used by the children to complete each sheet, it is recommended that you engage in some oral maths work with the class before they start. A varied use of mathematical vocabulary is very important when doing this. Some brief guidance for this aspect of your lesson preparation is given alongside each worksheet heading on the 'Teacher's information chart' on the opposite page. (You will find other suitable oral maths activities described in detail in the Scholastic teachers' book *Developing Mental Maths with 9–11 year olds*.)

RECORD-KEEPING

The photocopiable record sheet on the next page is to facilitate your record-keeping and assessment. This can either be given to the child as a record of his or her achievement or used as a teacher's record of which pages have been completed by which children and with what degree of success.

CONTENT ORGANIZATION

Each book is split into four sections:
A Counting and ordering
B Addition and subtraction
C Multiplication and division
D Multistep and mixed operations

The activities on each worksheet in sections A–C concentrate on one strategy, offering instant recall practice, number and word problems and a more investigational extension activity. The intention is that the page represents an 'achievable minimum' for children working at that level and that the extension activity (indicated by the icon 📓) will only be attempted by the more able child using a separate maths book or blank paper which can then be included in his or her personal maths file. In this way, it is hoped that the less able child will be able to tackle the majority of the page, while the more able child also has a 'special challenge'.

At the end of each of the first three sections (A–C) you will find two review tests relating specifically to the content of the sheets in that section. The problems are numbered to key in with the worksheet pages to which the questions relate. These review sheets will provide you with an opportunity to assess how well each child is progressing with the strategies on the worksheets in that section.

The final section of worksheets (D) gives the children the chance to practise some of their developing skills using more involved mental operation sequences that often require them to hold on to an interim number. The sheets in this section will really challenge the children.

ANSWERS

The final pages of the book provide the answers to all, but the most open-ended, of the questions on each worksheet. Answers in bold indicate those numbers which are given on the worksheets.

ABOUT THIS BOOK

Quick Mental Maths for 11 year olds is intended for Year 6/P7 children working at NC/NIC Level 4/5 (NNP Year 6) or confidently within Scottish Level D/E.

It is hoped the activities in this book will help to consolidate the children's knowledge and understanding of place value, counting and times tables and that it will lead them into adopting some of the many different strategies available to them for tackling daily mathematical situations with confidence and efficiency.

RECORD SHEET

SHEET NO	MARK	COMMENT
A1		
A2		
A3		
A4		
A5		
A6		
A7		
B1		
B2		
B3		
B4		
B5		
B6		
B7		
B8		
B9		
B10		
B11		
B12		
B13		
B14		

SHEET NO	MARK	COMMENT
C1		
C2		
C3		
C4		
C5		
C6		
C7		
C8		
C9		
C10		
C11		
C12		
C13		
C14		
D1		
D2		
D3		
D4		

COUNTING IN STEPS (INC NEGATIVE NUMBERS)

1. Complete these sequences of numbers.

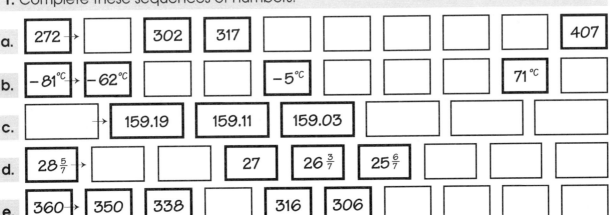

a. | 272 → | | 302 | 317 | | | | | | 407 |

b. | −81 °C → | −62 °C | | | −5 °C | | | | 71 °C | |

c. | | → 159.19 | 159.11 | 159.03 | | | |

d. | $28\frac{5}{7}$ → | | | 27 | $26\frac{3}{7}$ | $25\frac{6}{7}$ | | | |

e. | 360 → | 350 | 338 | | 316 | 306 | | | |

2. Count back in 125s from the number at the start of the line until you reach the number at the end.

a. 42 250 _____ 41 250

b. 1025 _____ 25

Count forwards in 5000s from the number at the start of the line until you reach the number at the end.

c. 12 628 _____ 47 628

d. 130 307 _____ 160 307

3. Shade in the numbers on the number square that are multiples of 2, 4 and 6.

a.

10	20	30	40	50	60	70
80	90	100	110	120	130	140
150	160	170	180	190	200	210
220	230	240	250	260	270	280
290	300	310	320	330	340	350
360	370	380	390	400	410	420
430	440	450	460	470	480	490

Continue counting upwards in 10s from 490 and write down in words the next two numbers that would be multiples of 2, 4 and 6.

b.
_____

Now answer these questions about the number square.

Which numbers are exactly divisible by 3 and 4?

c. _____

Which numbers are multiples of 5 and 10?

d. _____

 Starting at 9999 count forward eight steps and then back eight steps in these amounts: 11, 15, 19, 21. Make up some number sequences using your own rules. Then ask a friend if he or she can work out what your rules are.

PLACE VALUE

COUNTING AND ORDERING

1. Write these amounts in figures.

a. six hundred and one _____

b. four thousand and nine _____

c. twenty thousand, six
hundred and three _____

d. one million, six hundred and twenty-
six thousand, four hundred and
ninety-one

_____

e. four hundred and seven thousand,
one hundred and seven

_____

f. twenty-six thousand,
three hundred _____

g. three hundred thousand _____

h. four thousand,
nine hundred _____

i. two million, four hundred and seven
thousand, five hundred and
eighty- three

_____

j. fifty-three thousand,
seven hundred and twenty-four

_____

k. eighty thousand and five _____

l. six hundred and ten _____

m. eighty thousand,
five hundred _____

n. twenty thousand, six
hundred and thirty _____

o. four thousand
and ninety _____

2. Write these amounts in words.

a. 3020 _____

b. 8200 _____

c. 5002 _____

d. 27 506 _____

e. 708 090 _____

f. 4 780 909 _____

How many:

g. thousands in 1 275 320? _____

h. hundreds in 4 008 957? _____

i. tens in 2 697 000? _____

3. Write the decimal fractions equivalent
to these amounts.

a. three tenths_____

b. 5 hundredths_____

c. 12 thousandths _____

d. 8 tenths _____

e. 200 thousandths_____

f. $\frac{23}{100}$_____

g. $\frac{4}{20}$ _____

h. forty hundredths _____

Using seven different digits, make up
ten seven-digit numbers. Write down
each number in words. Arrange the
numbers in a column according to size,
starting with the smallest.

ORDERING WHOLE, FRACTIONAL AND % AMOUNTS

1. Write a number in each empty box so that the six numbers in each stack are in order.

a.
99 999
106 328
342 057

b.
720 490
720 488
635 731

c.
500 000
750 000
999 999

3. Choose suitable fractions with different denominators to make these number sentences complete.

a. $\frac{3}{7} >$ ☐   **c.** $\frac{5}{9} <$ ☐

b. $\frac{8}{16} =$ ☐   **d.** $\frac{15}{20} =$ ☐

In each box, write an appropriate decimal fraction to two or three decimal places.

e. 8 > ☐

f. 2.3 < ☐

g. 126.27cm < ☐

h. 91.098km > ☐

i. 3570.4kg > ☐

j. £76.55 < ☐

k. 60.001g > ☐

2. Work out these calculations and then place one of the following three signs between each sum: < > or =

a. 200 ÷ 10 _____ 150 × 10

b. − 3 + 23 _____ 42 − 31

c. 150 − 91 _____ 56 + 61

d. 81 ÷ 9 _____ − 4 + 13

e. 48 ÷ 8 _____ 7 × 8

f. 55 + 56 _____ 41 + 63

g. 140 − 38 _____ 6 × 9

h. 4 × 8 _____ 74 + 73

i. 25 × 5 _____ 135 − 39

j. 33 + 28 _____ 87 − 26

k. − 74 + 100 _____ 300 ÷ 5

l. 9 × 20 _____ 10 × 170

m. 250 ÷ 5 _____ 118 − 91

n. 66 + 74 _____ 6 × 25

o. 27 + 101 _____ 149 − 16

p. − 50 + 49 _____ − 33 + 32

q. 7 × 9 _____ 96 − 28

r. 81 ÷ 3 _____ 11 + 16

s. 135 − 41 _____ 32 + 49

Work out the answers to these problems.

l. $\frac{12}{24}$ = _____ %

m. 25% = _____ eighths

 $\frac{1}{2} = \frac{2}{4} = \frac{3}{6} = \frac{4}{8} = \frac{5}{10} = \frac{6}{12} = \frac{7}{14} = \frac{8}{16} = \frac{9}{18} = \frac{10}{20}$. Now write down the fraction patterns for the following unit fractions in the same way as the example given. $\frac{1}{3} \ \frac{1}{4} \ \frac{1}{5} \ \frac{1}{6} \ \frac{1}{7} \ \frac{1}{8} \ \frac{1}{9} \ \frac{1}{10}$

COUNTING AND ORDERING

ESTIMATING AND APPROXIMATING

1. Write the answer to each sum in the first box. Then choose from the list below the amount that is closest to the actual answer and write that in the second box.

0.75   950   5   400   0.5   210   0.075   4   500   1000   750   550

a. $480 + 480$ =

b. $1600 \div 8$ =

c. $£625 - £79$ =

d. $-170 + 600$ =

e. $73 \div 1000$ =

f. $3007 - 1996$ =

g. $73m \div 100$ =

h. $260 + 260$ =

i. $0.8g \times 0.6$ =

j. $-3260 + 4000$ =

k. $£39 \div 10$ =

l. 6×0.8 =

2. Estimate the numbers marked by the arrows on these number lines.

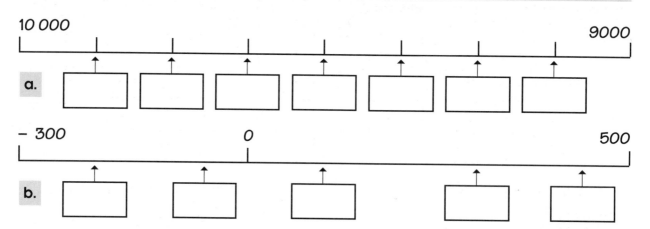

10 000   9000

a.

$- 300$ 0   500

b.

3. Circle the two values that are roughly the same in each row.

a. $\frac{1}{2}$ 35%   0.49   0.02

b. 0.83 $\frac{7}{16}$ $\frac{3}{8}$ 90%

c. 30%   3.3   0.04 $\frac{3}{100}$

d. $\frac{3}{4}$ 74%   0.034   0.34

e. 0.09 $\frac{3}{9}$ $\frac{8}{12}$ 33%

f. 71%   0.17   7.171 $\frac{7}{10}$

Make up some estimation questions to ask your friends. You could ask questions such as how many bricks in a particular wall or how many word entries on a page in a dictionary. What methods did your friends use to calculate the answers?

P

QUICK MENTAL MATHS

ROUNDING WHOLE NUMBERS AND DECIMALS

1. Round these amounts to the nearest:

a. £100	**b.** 1000 kilometres	**c.** 10 000 miles
£4251 _____	500 ½ km _____	52 836 miles _____
£36 749 _____	3499km _____	460 001 miles _____
£843 001 _____	8620.3km _____	790 999 miles _____
£949.99 _____	483 995km _____	854 030 miles _____

d. Round these lengths to the nearest centimetre.

851mm _____ 376mm _____ 4439mm _____ 7904mm _____

2. In column X write the answer to each sum. In column Y write the answer rounded to the nearest £.

	£		£			X	Y
a.	2.50	+	8.70	=			
b.	30.06	−	28.97	=			
c.	7.95	−	3.86	=			
d.	15.52	+	14.25	=			
e.	6.42	−	3.43	=			
f.	4.80	+	4.80	=			

	£					X	Y
g.	4.70	×	2	=			
h.	3.78	÷	3	=			
i.	6.20	×	4	=			
j.	11.00	÷	2	=			
k.	10.90	×	0.5	=			
l.	3.50	×	7	=			

3. Round these amounts to the nearest whole number.

a. 4.26 _____ 17.36 _____ 72.019 _____
b. 9.75 _____ 58.01 _____ 845.01 _____
c. 3.49 _____ 25.25 _____ 924.99 _____
d. 7.99 _____ 42.50 _____ 37.005 _____
e. 2.51 _____ 36.89 _____ 45.989 _____

Round these amounts to the nearest tenth.

f. 2.38 _____ 57.366 _____
g. 6.85 _____ 34.893 _____
h. 3.63 _____ 73.499 _____
i. 5.21 _____ 42.425 _____
j. 4.04 _____ 85.270 _____

Write down some examples of amounts you would round to the nearest 10, 100, 1000, 10 000, 100 000 or 1 000 000. For instance, the crowd at a Grand Prix would be rounded to the nearest 1000.

TEST YOUR SKILLS 1 (A1–A3)

COUNTING AND ORDERING

A1 Fill in the missing numbers in these sequences.

a. | | → | | | | −10 | | | | | | −280 | | −370 |

b. | 570 | → | 585 | | 595 | | | | 620 | | 635 | | | | |

c. | | → | | | 239.90 | | 239.97 | | | | 240.11 |

d. | $63\frac{5}{9}$ | → | 63 | | $62\frac{4}{9}$ | | | | | | |

e. | | → | 67°C | | | | | | | −28°C | | −47°C |

f. | 489 | → | | | | 429 | | 414 | | | | |

A2 Write in one figure the number that has all the following amounts in it.

a. 7 hundreds   5 tens   492 thousands   3 million   8 units _____

How many:

b. hundreds in   thousands in   tens in
    3 268 302? _____   5 097 040? _____   5 097 040? _____

Write these amounts in figures.

c. four hundred and two _____

d. six thousand and 51 _____

e. thirty thousand, seven
    hundred and eight _____

f. 80 thousand _____

g. nine hundred and thirty-six
    thousand, four hundred and
    fifteen

    _____

h. ten million, five
    hundred thousand
    and twenty _____

A3 Write a number in each empty box so that the five numbers in each stack are in order.

a. | $2\frac{1}{8}$ |
   | |
   | $2\frac{4}{16}$ |
   | |
   | $2\frac{3}{8}$ |

b. | 50.02 |
   | |
   | 50 |
   | |
   | 49.98 |

c. | |
   | 30 000 |
   | |
   | 30 002 |
   | |

d. | 300 001 |
   | |
   | |
   | |
   | 299 997 |

TOTAL

TEST YOUR SKILLS 2 (A4–A5)

A4 Write the answer to each sum in the first box. Then choose from the list below the amount that is closest to the actual answer and write that in the second box.

500   200   600   12.50   0.7   0.6   325   2050   6   2000

a. 290 + 290 = ☐ ☐   **f.** 4080 − 2090 = ☐ ☐

b. 0.9g × 0.7 = ☐ ☐   **g.** −190 + 400 = ☐ ☐

c. £565 − £88 = ☐ ☐   **h.** £126 ÷ 10 = ☐ ☐

d. 72m ÷ 100 = ☐ ☐   **i.** 5009 − 2957 = ☐ ☐

e. 7 × 0.8 = ☐ ☐   **j.** 247p + 75p = ☐ ☐

Estimate the numbers marked by the arrows on these number lines.

10 000   10 910

k. | 10 130 | ☐ | ☐ | ☐ | ☐ | ☐ |

−200   0   500

l. ☐   ☐   ☐   ☐

A5 Round these amounts to the nearest:

a. ☐ cm   789mm _____   **c.** ☐ 1000kg   599 ½ kg _____
                504mm _____   44 499kg _____
                3256mm _____   90 500kg _____

b. ☐ £100   £7949 _____   **d.** ☐ 10 000km   63 999km _____
                £252 006 _____   5025km _____
                £54 549.99 _____   380 004km _____

e. Round these amounts to the nearest whole number.

6. 19 ☐   84.51 ☐

f. Round these amounts to the nearest tenth.

8.83 ☐   5.426 ☐

QUICK MENTAL MATHS

TOTAL ☐

COUNTING AND ORDERING

ADDITION FACTS

1. Work out the missing amounts in these addition facts.

a. 270cm + 270cm = ☐

b. 565km + ☐ = 1390km

c. ☐ + 570ml = 1410ml

d. 8200g + 8900g = ☐

e. 55cm + ☐ = 100cm

f. ☐ + 330kg = 1010kg

g. 305mm + 875mm = ☐

h. 46 min + ☐ = 92 min

i. ☐ + 740km = 1480km

j. £6900 + £7200 = ☐

k. 760m + ☐ = 1520m

l. ☐ + 635cm = 1010cm

2. Using multiples of 5 or 10, write in figures two two-digit numbers that add up to the amounts shown below. The first one has been done for you.

a. 130 __95 + 35__   g. 155 _____
b. 135 _____   h. 180 _____
c. 120 _____   i. 185 _____
d. 175 _____   j. 150 _____
e. 140 _____   k. 115 _____
f. 145 _____   l. 160 _____

Do the same again, but this time use two two-digit numbers that are *not* multiples of 5 or 10. Write each number in words.

m. 117 _____
n. 182 _____
o. 163 _____

3. Solve the problems below.

a. A length of wool was cut into 3 shorter lengths measuring 26cm, 38cm and 17cm. What was the total length of the original piece of wool? _____

b. Add together two thousand, four hundred and fifty and 7390. _____

c. What number has a total of 860 when added to itself? _____

d. Double 4700g and give your answer in kg. _____

Fill in the missing numbers in this table.

+	4300	8400
1500		9900
5900		
6800	11100	
3200		
9600		
7700		16100

Draw an addition table like the one above. Write the same numbers in the left-hand column but replace the two numbers across the top with 1976 and 2857. Now fill in the table.

QUICK MENTAL MATHS

SUBTRACTION FACTS

1. Think carefully about place value when working out these number sentences. (They are not too difficult!)

a. $8 - 0.962 =$ _____

b. $11 - 0.631 =$ _____

c. $13 - 0.464 =$ _____

d. $4 - 0.247 =$ _____

e. $1 - 0.478 =$ _____

f. $9 - 0.152 =$ _____

g. $3 - 0.835 =$ _____

h. $6 - 0.581 =$ _____

i. $10 - 0.386 =$ _____

j. $16 - 0.492 =$ _____

k. $14 - 0.646 =$ _____

l. $5 - 0.393 =$ _____

Subtract any two-digit number from any three-digit number to give the answer shown. The first one has been done for you.

m. $\boxed{121} - \boxed{48}$ = seventy-three

n. $\boxed{} - \boxed{}$ = sixty-eight

o. $\boxed{} - \boxed{}$ = fifty-seven

p. $\boxed{} - \boxed{}$ = forty-five

2. Work out the missing amounts in these subtraction problems.

a. $85cm - 36cm = \boxed{}$

b. $\boxed{} - 4600m = 8900m$

c. $47kg - 23\frac{1}{2}kg = \boxed{}$

d. $£5620 - \boxed{} = £1780$

e. $\boxed{} - 49ml = 107ml$

f. $23\,000 - 1500 = \boxed{}$

g. $6793km - \boxed{} = 6353km$

h. $\boxed{} - 900 = 15100$

i. $725cm - 450cm = \boxed{}$

j. $1526kg - \boxed{} = 1056kg$

k. $\boxed{} - 19\frac{1}{2}hrs = 19\frac{1}{2}hrs$

l. $4500m - 695m = \boxed{}$

3a. Fill in the missing numbers in this table and solve the problems below.

–	3173	5284
630		4654
820		
570	2603	
750		
420		
940		4344

b. What must be taken away from eight to make seven point six five? _____

c. How much less is an item costing £3.73 than an item costing £8.50? _____

d. The approximate flying distance between two cities is 1100km. The actual distance is 989km. Find the difference. _____

e. From a million subtract 264 000. _____

 Draw a subtraction table like the one above. Add 500 to each of the numbers in the left-hand column and 50 to each number in the row across the top. Fill in the table using these new amounts.

ADDITION AND SUBTRACTION

RELATIONSHIP BETWEEN + AND –

1. Fill in the answer and then write out each set of related calculations in the same way as the first one has been done.

a. 3009 – 450 = _2559_   3009 – 2559 = 450, 450 + 2559 = 3009, 2559 + 450 = 3009

b. 256 + 475 = _____ _____

c. 7800 + 1700 = _____ _____

d. 4060 – 1300 = _____ _____

e. 329 + 5472 = _____ _____

2. Join two numbers to each number box so that they make a correct addition calculation. Write out the sum. Then change the numbers round in each calculation to make two subtraction facts. Look at how the first one has been done.

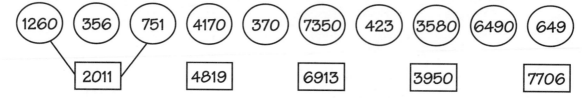

(1260) (356) (751) (4170) (370) (7350) (423) (3580) (6490) (649)

[2011]   [4819]   [6913]   [3950]   [7706]

___1260 + 751 = 2011___   ___2011 – 1260 = 751___   ___2011 – 751 = 1260___

_____   _____   _____

_____   _____   _____

_____   _____   _____

_____   _____   _____

3. In the right-hand box, write an addition fact using all three numbers from the left-hand box.

In the right-hand box, write a subtraction fact using all three numbers from the left-hand box.

a.

189, 2730, 2919	2730 + 189 = 2919
5950, 290, 5660	
574, 8824, 8250	
9830, 10 002, 172	

b.

5007, 860, 4147	5007 – 860 = 4147
5230, 2800, 8030	
390, 7450, 7060	
880, 5800, 6680	

Using the numbers 3005, 259, 2715, 567, 826 and 290, make up as many three figure addition and subtraction statements as you can, for example, 567 + 259 = 826.

ADDITION AND SUBTRACTION

PAIRS AND DOUBLES

1. Write the amount that needs to be added to each number to make 700.

a. 180 _____   230_____   360 _____   440 _____   570 _____   350 _____

b. 382 _____   574 _____   493 _____   367 _____   224 _____   145 _____

Now write the amount that needs to be added to each number to make 2250.

c. 983 _____   475_____   1240 _____   1370 _____   636 _____

d. 1540 _____   291 _____   598 _____   862 _____   1911 _____

2. Read the value of the numbers carefully then work out the answers to these problems. Write your answers in words.

a. Seventy thousand add ninety thousand. _____

b. Decrease sixty-six thousand by thirty-nine thousand. _____

c. What number is added to two hundred and thirty-seven thousand to make three hundred and one thousand? _____

d. Subtract four hundred and twenty thousand from a million and add five hundred and sixty-four to the answer. _____

e. Combine forty-seven thousand with ten thousand, two hundred and eight and subtract two hundred and nine from your answer. _____

3. Double the first amount and then double that answer. The first one has been done for you.

560	1120	2240
750		
970		

660		
890		
470		

380		
870		
740		

Make a list of the numbers from 1050 to 1100. Next to each number write down its double. Carry on past 1100 if you have time.

QUICK MENTAL MATHS

ADDING ORDER

1. Rearrange these calculations in your head so that you start with the largest amount. Remember to look for number bonds.

a. 14 + 40 + 1210 + 56 + 17 = _____   g. 320km + 426km + 1580km = _____

b. 38 + 40 + 27 + 2750 + 33 = _____   h. 770kg + 4030kg + 659kg = _____

c. 32 + 20 + 9120 + 68 + 81 = _____   i. £942 + £840 + £9360 = _____

d. 60 + 25 + 45 + 56 + 8530 = _____   j. 220ml + 6780ml + 50ml = _____

e. 71 + 19 + 73 + 10 + 3940 = _____   k. £620 + £5220 + £360 = _____

f. 45 + 6480 + 70 + 42 + 58 = _____   l. 405m + 555m + 7550m = _____

2. Answer these questions. Think about putting the largest number first.

a. What amount results from adding £2.40, £4.60, £1.25 and £1.75? _____

b. Find the total of six, sixty, six hundred and six thousand and six. _____

c. Increase four hundred and seventy by five thousand, three hundred and thirty and increase the result by one million, three hundred and ten. _____

d. Make up a number sentence of 4 numbers with each figure having a different number of digits. _____

3. Make up ten addition sums. Use each of these numbers once. Use three numbers in each sum. Put the largest number first.

105	215	420	320	945
530	465	635	780	570
675	740	990	210	425
845	630	950	120	735
840	315	195	150	225
255	330	360	885	525

 Make up some of your own addition sums using four three-digit multiples of 5. Write down each sum placing the largest number first. Then calculate the answer mentally and write it down.

IDENTIFYING NEAR DOUBLES AND TREBLES

1. Look at these examples which are here to help you with your thinking.

4000 + 3900 = 7900. This calculation can be done by thinking: *double 4000 minus 100.*
2500 + 2550 = 5050. This calculation can be done by thinking: *double 2500 plus 50.*

Now add these near doubles. Use the examples above to help you with your *thinking.*

a. 6000m + 5850m =

b. 4250km + 4300km =

c. £7550 + £7500 =

d. 8750g + 9000g =

e. 5250kg + 5000kg =

f. £3125 + £3100 =

2. Here are two other ways to *think* when adding near doubles. There are other ways not shown here.

7900 + 7800 = 8000 + 8000 − 100 − 200 = 15 700
6000 + 5000 = 6000 + 6000 − 1000 or 5000 + 5000 + 1000 = 11 000

Write out your thinking process when you do these calculations.

a. 25 000 + 24 700 = _____

b. 38 000 + 37 000 = _____

c. 46 800 + 46 900 = _____

3. You can use similar methods when adding three numbers. Look at this example.

5700 + 5900 + 5800 = 6000 + 6000 + 6000 − 300 − 100 − 200 = 17 400

Now try to do questions **a–c** in the same way. Choose a different way to answer question **d**. Tell your teacher how you did it.

a. 7500 + 7900 + 7700 =

b. 8750 + 8950 + 8850 =

c. 6650 + 6850 + 6950 =

d. 3200 + 3300 + 3400 =

Make up ten addition sums that have three five-digit numbers close to each other in value. Show all the thinking stages that lead to the final answer.

CALCULATION PATTERNS (+ AND –)

1. Complete these calculation grids in the way indicated. Read the tip below first. When filling in the grids, add/subtract multiples of 10 and then adjust by 1.

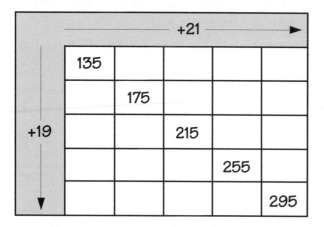

+21 →

135				
	175			
		215		
			255	
				295

+19 ↓

–31 →

				875
			877	
		879		
	881			
883				

–29 ↓

2. Look at these addition squares and then fill them in.
The first one has been done for you.

1250	2850	4100
940	1350	2290
2190	4200	6390

	1205	1960
245		2250
	3210	

8700	2400	
	4900	8520
12,320		

3. Study these subtraction grids carefully, complete them and then answer the question below.

–	7100	8200	9300
2600			6700
3700		4500	
4800		3400	
5900	1200		

–	624	734	844
150	474		
260		474	
370		364	
480			364

What do you notice about the number patterns in the subtraction grids you have just completed?

_____

Look carefully at the number patterns in the subtraction grids you completed in part 3. Now, using different numbers, make up two number grids of your own that have the same number patterns.

QUICK MENTAL MATHS

PARTITIONING AND RECOMBINING

1. The calculation below shows the *thinking* stages for finding the correct answer.

356 + 475 = 300 + 400 + 50 + 70 + 6 + 5 = 700 + 120 + 11 = 831

Do these two calculations and write out all the *thinking stages* in the same way as the example above.

a. 537 + 284 = _____

b. 168 + 642 = _____

Study this calculation.

478 + 453 = 478 + 22 + 431 = 500 + 431 = 931

Do the first sum in the same way, then try to *think* like that for the others.

c. 386 + 547 = _____

d. 175 + 669 = _____   **e.** 887 + 112 = _____   **f.** 584 + 343 = _____

2. Look at the completed grid below. Read it from left to right and top to bottom as you would a book. Now fill in the other two grids in the same way.

	683	+	798		
=	600	+	700		
+	80	+	90		
+	3	+	8		
=	1300	+	170	+	11
=	1481				

	969	+	557		
=		+			
+		+			
+		+			
=		+		+	
=					

		+			
=	700	+			
+		+	60		
+	5	+			
=		+		+	
=	1610				

3. Use any of the *thinking stages* shown above to work out the answers to these problems. To help you remember, write down the answers to each stage as you go along.

a. Find the total of 392 and four hundred and sixty-eight _____

b. Make eight hundred and sixty larger by 756. _____

 Draw some grids like those in part 2 and write in some four-digit numbers. You will need an extra row of boxes and an extra column on the right. Try using five-digit numbers or even larger amounts.

BRIDGING AND ADJUSTING

1. The four examples below show the *thinking* stages for finding the correct answer.

$$384 + 285 = 384 + 300 - 15 = 684 - 15 = 669$$
$$5635 + 3983 = 5635 + 4000 - 17 = 9635 - 17 = 9618$$
$$754 - 288 = 754 - 300 + 12 = 454 + 12 = 466$$
$$4268 - 1974 = 4268 - 2000 + 26 = 2268 + 26 = 2294$$

Write out your thinking stages when you answer these problems. Try to use the strategies outlined above.

a. 638m + 479m = _____

b. 914kg – 587kg = _____

c. £4523 – £2791 = _____

d. 3746km + 8973km = _____

2. Here are some more ways of *thinking* when adding and subtracting.

$5465 + 7186 = 5465 + 7000 + 100 + 80 + 6 = 12\,465 + 100 + 80 + 6 = 12\,651$
$8372 - 5594 = 8372 - 5000 - 500 - 90 - 4 = 3372 - 500 - 90 - 4$ $= 2872 - 90 - 4 = 2782 - 4 = 2778$

Do these calculations in the same way, showing your *thinking* stages.

a. 6493 – 2367 =	
b. 3386 + 9527 =	

3. Solve these problems using some of the strategies on this page. Write down interim numbers if it helps.

a. Find the difference between £8259 and £2983. _____

b. Work out the total length in metres of 756cm and 988cm. _____

    Work with a friend. Ask him or her to write down a three-digit number. You then choose a three-digit number to add to it. Your friend does the sum showing all the thinking stages. You check the answer. Swap roles.

ADDITION AND SUBTRACTION

B9

+ AND – WHOLE, FRACTIONAL, DECIMAL AND % AMOUNTS

1. Work out the answers to these calculations. Do the parts in brackets first. Try various strategies.

a. (38m + 26m) – 52m = [ ]

b. 120km – (34km + 47km) = [ ]

c. £1350 + (£1240 – £325) = [ ]

d. (720kg – 85kg) + 15kg = [ ]

h. (373ml + 97ml) – 71ml = [ ]

i. 5006km – 17km – 103km = [ ]

j. 260cm + 350cm + 190cm = [ ]

k. (37hrs + 45hrs) – 33hrs = [ ]

e. How much must be added to £82.32 to make £90.00? _____

f. What is the difference between 280 and the sum of seventy-five and fifty? _____

g. Find a quarter of a million, double the answer and add 150 000 to the result.

Give the answer in words. _____

2. Look at the way the first fraction problem has been done. Now work out the others in the same way by finding the common denominator.

a. $\frac{1}{4} + \frac{1}{3} = \frac{3+4}{12} = \boxed{\frac{7}{12}}$

b. $\frac{4}{5} + \frac{7}{10} = \frac{\quad + \quad}{} = \boxed{}$

c. $\frac{1}{2} - \frac{3}{8} = \frac{\quad - \quad}{} = \boxed{}$

d. $\frac{1}{2} - \frac{3}{10} = \frac{\quad - \quad}{} = \boxed{}$

e. $\frac{4}{5} + \frac{1}{2} = \frac{\quad + \quad}{} = \boxed{}$

f. $\frac{7}{12} + \frac{3}{4} = \frac{\quad + \quad}{} = \boxed{}$

g. $\frac{5}{8} - \frac{1}{4} = \frac{\quad - \quad}{} = \boxed{}$

h. $\frac{7}{10} - \frac{3}{5} = \frac{\quad - \quad}{} = \boxed{}$

3. Give the answers in £ for the first table and in m for the second.

+	68p	97p	69p	58p	76p	66p	49p	57p	86p	47p	78p
£5.75			£6.44								

–	96cm	32cm	55cm	64cm	48cm	62cm	41cm	33cm	57cm	81cm	79cm
4.8m							4.39m				

 Find 20%, 25% and 85% of these amounts: 400, 700, 2000, 3500 and 10 000.

PLACE VALUE WHEN ADDING AND SUBTRACTING

1. Write the answers to these questions in words. Think carefully about the best mental strategy to use to find the answer. You might find it helpful to jot down the numbers in figures to help you with your mental calculations!

a. Twenty-six thousand and fifty add four
thousand, one hundred and fifty is equal to _____

b. Twenty-five thousand, four hundred
minus six thousand, five hundred is the same as _____

c. Total up three hundred and seven thousand, four hundred
and ninety and one thousand, three hundred and ten. _____

d. From four hundred and twenty-nine thousand,
eight hundred and sixty subtract 3155. _____

e. To three million, three hundred add eight million and thirty. _____

2. Write down the answer in the first box. In the second box, give the value of the 8 in each answer.

a. 3.34 + 0.48 = ☐ ☐   **d.** 12 000 − 3750 = ☐ ☐

b. 16.68 − 2.10 = ☐ ☐   **e.** 23 + 38 + 37 = ☐ ☐

c. 2900 + 1900 = ☐ ☐   **f.** 0.400 − 0.122 = ☐ ☐

3. Write the answers in the first column. In the second column, arrange the answers as indicated in each table.

1050 491 + 9	1050 500	Largest
1505 009 − 4		
1005 044 + 6		
1055 063 − 8		
1050 057 − 7		Smallest

404 424 − 20		Smallest
440 044 − 40		
440 350 + 50		
404 410 + 30		
404 074 − 30		Largest

Look at the numbers you have placed in order in the second column in the tables above. Write them out in words.

ADDING AND SUBTRACTING SEVERAL NUMBERS

B12

1. Do these sums by using strategies such as looking for number bonds or starting with the largest amount.

a. 14cm + 36cm + 27cm = _____

b. _____ + 17ml + 43ml = 94ml

c. 25km + _____ + 35km = 98km

d. 14kg + 26kg + _____ = 94kg

e. £13.00 + £28.00 + £52.00 = _____

f. 160mm + 750mm + 910mm = _____

g. £690.00 + £210.00 + _____ = £1350.00

h. 320kg + _____ + 370kg = 1310kg

2. Study the table below and then fill in the empty spaces in the same way.

−	1610	1650	1910	1750	1520	1510	1720	1830	1840	1540	1630
160	1450			1590				1670	1680	1380	
170	1440				1350	1340					1460
190		1460				1320			1650		
	10		30			20	30		30		

3. The shapes below show parts of the number grid. Each shape has numbers that add up to 100. Use the number grid to help you fill in all the shapes. The first one has been done for you.

5	25	25
25	20	a.

10	5	15	10	5
20	30	5	25	25
15	5	25	20	15
20	10	20	30	10
15	30	25	5	30

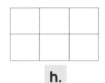

b.

g.

h.

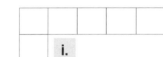

i.

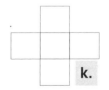

c.

d.

e.

f.

j.

k.

 Here's a mental addition challenge! Add up the four numbers in each column of the table in part 2. Here's another mental challenge! Add up all the numbers shown in the number grid above.

NAME _____   CLASS _____

TEST YOUR SKILLS 1 (B1–B6)

ADDITION AND SUBTRACTION

B1 Find the total of each pair of numbers. Think about the different strategies you can use.

a. 95 + 95 = _____   464 + 76 = _____   2600 + 2600 = _____

b. 48 + 57 = _____   568 + 490 = _____   3720 + 4263 = _____

c. 75 + 80 = _____   330 + 275 = _____   670 + 4259 = _____

d. 63 + 56 = _____   59 + 520 = _____   5800 + 3900 = _____

B2 Solve the problems below.

a. From 2 000 000 subtract 371 000. _____

b. Decrease 5500km by seven hundred and ninety-five km. _____

B3 Write out the four related addition and subtraction facts for each of these sets of numbers.

a. 898, 2901, 2003   _____ _____

_____ _____

b. 8040, 5650, 2390   _____ _____

_____ _____

B4 Double the first amount and then double that answer. The first one has been done for you.

470	940	1880
730		

550		
990		

680		
860		

B5 Make up four addition sums using three numbers. Use all the numbers. Put the largest number first.

525	150	950	740	530	675
845	840	255	330	360	885

_____ _____

_____ _____

B6 4800 + 4900 = (5000 + 5000) − 200 − 100 = 9700. Do the following sum in the same way.

£3700 + £3900 = _____

QUICK MENTAL MATHS

TOTAL

TEST YOUR SKILLS 2 (B7–B12)

B7 Study these addition squares carefully and then complete them.

	4750	6070
450		990
	5290	

480	1320	
	370	2230
2340		

Fill in the subtraction grid below. You will notice a pattern developing with the numbers.

−	7120	7230	7340	8450	8560	8670
2505						

B8 Supply the missing numbers in the *thinking* stages of these two calculations.

a. 437 + 568 = ____ + 500 +____ + 60 + 7 +____ =____ + 90 + 15 = 1005

b. 486 + 257 = ____ + 14 + 243 = 500 + ____ = 743

B9 Fill in the *thinking* stages in these two calculations.

a. 283m + 588m = 283m + 600m − ____ m = ____ m − 12m = 871m

b. 837g − 589g = ____ g − 600g + 11g = 237g + ____ g = ____ g

B10 Work out these fractions by first finding the common denominator.

a. $\frac{2}{3} + \frac{2}{5}$ = $\dfrac{\quad + \quad}{}$ = ☐   b. $\frac{3}{4} - \frac{3}{8}$ = $\dfrac{\quad - \quad}{}$ = ☐

Find the answers to the following problems.

c. (27 + 46) − 35 ____   d. £5.65 + 48p ____   e. 5.6m − 69cm ____

B11 Write the answer in the first box. In the second box, give the value of the 2 in the answer.

a. 4.64 + 0.38 = ☐ ☐   b. 18.80 − 6.35 = ☐ ☐

B12 Choose a sensible strategy to help you resolve this problem.

Subtract 45 and 65 from 130 and add the answer to 46 add 24. ____

ADDITION AND SUBTRACTION

B14

MULTIPLICATION AND DIVISION

MULTIPLICATION FACTS

1. Work out the missing amounts in these multiplication problems.

a. [ ] × 7 = 140cm

b. 30 × [ ] = 270km

c. 8 × 40ml = [ ]

d. 6g × [ ] = 300g

e. [ ] × 6 = 240 ltrs

f. 8 × [ ] = 240kg

g. 20mm × 9 = [ ]

h. 60 min × [ ] = 360 min

i. [ ] × 90 = 540km

j. 9 × [ ] = 540cm

k. £70 × 10 = [ ]

l. 10 × [ ] = 500m

2. Find the product of each pair of numbers. The first one has been done for you.

a. 70, 40 __2800__

b. 50, 90 _____

c. 80, 80 _____

d. 20, 90 _____

e. 40, 60 _____

f. 60, 70 _____

g. 70, 50 _____

h. 40, 80 _____

i. 50, 50 _____

j. 10, 60 _____

k. 60, 30 _____

l. 50, 80 _____

m. Fill in the missing numbers in this table using the £ sign.

×	£1.20	£1.50	£1.40	£1.30
7		£10.50		
5	£6.00			
9			£12.60	
8				£10.40
6		£9.00		

3. Solve the problems below.

a. In a large carton there were one thousand and fifty plastic cups. How many cups were there in seven cartons? _____

b. A medicine bottle when full holds enough medicine to fill an 8ml spoon 90 times. Work out the capacity of the medicine bottle in millilitres. _____

c. Multiply the product of six and seven by thirty. _____

d. Write the decimal number you get when you multiply nought point seven by nought point six. _____

Here's a mental challenge! Draw a multiplication grid 21 squares across and 21 squares down. Write the numbers 0-20 down the left-hand column and 0-20 across the top. Fill in your grid. Time yourself.

QUICK MENTAL MATHS

DIVISION FACTS

1. In each of these pairs of numbers divide the smaller number into the larger number.

a. 366, 6 _____   8, 728 _____   639, 9 _____

b. 2, 362 _____   606, 6 _____   6, 306 _____

c. 724, 4 _____   5, 855 _____   402, 2 _____

d. 5, 955 _____   462, 2 _____   7, 357 _____

e. 573, 3 _____   8, 568 _____   483, 3 _____

f. 8, 408 _____   524, 4 _____   8, 328 _____

g. Fill in the missing numbers in this division table.

÷	6400	10 400	13 600	16 800
20	320			840
40			340	
80		130		
÷	1080	1350	1620	1890
90				

2. Work out the missing amounts in these division calculations.

a. 120g ÷ 6 = [ ]

b. 480km ÷ [ ] = 60km

c. [ ] ÷ 9 = 80m

d. £630.00 ÷ [ ] = £90.00

e. 420m ÷ 6 = [ ]

f. £450.00 ÷ [ ] = £50.00

g. [ ] ÷ 7 = 70cm

h. 500km ÷ [ ] = 100km

i. 640 min ÷ 8 = [ ]

j. 280mm ÷ [ ] = 40mm

k. [ ] ÷ 4 = 90kg

l. 270ml ÷ [ ] = 30ml

3. Solve the problems below.

a. How many sixes in one hundred and twenty-six? _____

b. Divide 5.6 by 4. _____

c. Share seventy-five by six and give your answer as a decimal fraction. _____

d. Work out an eighth of 104. _____

e. Lily spent two fifths of her savings of £6.50. How much did she have left? _____

f. Fill in the missing numbers in this table.

÷	10.8	14.4	13.2
3	3.6		
6		2.4	
12			1.1
÷	1.08	1.44	1.32
3	0.36		
6			0.22

Start at 16 ÷ 16 = 1, 32 ÷ 16 = 2... and see how far you can get. Can you reach 320 ÷ 16 = 20? Do the same with 17, 18 and 19. Use the numbers you have just written out to help you with these.

QUICK MENTAL MATHS

RELATIONSHIP BETWEEN × AND ÷

1. Fill in the answer and then write out the set of missing related calculations in the same way as the first one has been done.

a. 1368 ÷ 8 = ___171___   1368 ÷ 171 = 8   8 × 171 = 1368   171 × 8 = 1368

b. 15 × 70 = _____   _____

c. 9 × 210 = _____   _____

d. 1350 ÷ 9 = _____   _____

e. 19 × 60 = _____   _____

2. Join two numbers to each number box to make a division calculation. Write out the sum. Now change the numbers round in each calculation to make two multiplication facts. Look at the one that's been done to help you.

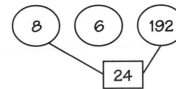

(8) (6) (192)   (171) (7) (115)   (9) (133) (138) (5)

[24]   [19]   [23]   [19]   [23]

192 ÷ 8 = 24   8 × 24 = 192   24 × 8 = 192

_____   _____   _____

_____   _____   _____

_____   _____   _____

_____   _____   _____

3. In the right-hand box, write two division facts using all three numbers from the left-hand box.

a.		
9, 1530, 170	1530 ÷ 9 = 170, 1530 ÷ 170 = 9
231, 8, 1848	
1190, 170, 7	
6, 241, 1446	

In the right-hand box, write two multiplication facts using all three numbers from the left-hand box.

b.		
1610, 230, 7	7 × 230 = 1610, 230 × 7 = 1610
9, 181, 1629	
190, 1520, 8	
1026, 6, 171	

Write out the four related multiplication and division facts for the 18 times table. Like this. 1 × 18 = 18, 18 × 1 = 18, 18 ÷ 1 = 18, 18 ÷ 18 = 1. Go as far as 20 × 18. Try with 16, 17 and 19.

DOUBLES, TREBLES AND FRACTIONAL AMOUNTS

1. Double the answers to these calculations.

a. 144cm ÷ 9 [ ]   600kg × 7 [ ]   154km ÷ 7 [ ]

Treble the answers to these calculations.

b. 5 × 80ml [ ]   £1260.00 ÷ 7 [ ]   70mm × 9 [ ]

Make these amounts twice the size.

c. 34 $\frac{1}{2}$ [ ]   27 $\frac{1}{2}$ [ ]   45 $\frac{1}{2}$ [ ]   19 $\frac{1}{2}$ [ ]

2. Larger numbers can be doubled by using the method shown in the example below. Look at it carefully.

Double 386 can be made easier by thinking: 600 + 160 + 12 = 772

Double these numbers in the same way. Write down your thinking stages.

a. 177 _____   **c.** 486 _____

b. 381 _____   **d.** 279 _____

3. Work out:

a. six tenths of: 70 ____   25 ____   350 ____   52 ____   1030 ____

b. three quarters of: 84 ____   96 ____   760 ____   68 ____   9200 ____

c. five eighths of: 72 ____   88 ____   144 ____   32 ____   5600 ____

Think carefully before answering the problems below.

d. What fraction of £1 is 45p? _____   **g.** Divide 4.2 by seven. _____

e. What fraction of 1m is 28cm? _____   **h.** Multiply $\frac{1}{2}$ by $\frac{1}{4}$ _____

f. What fraction of 1km is 250m? _____   **i.** 0.7 times 0.8 = _____

Choose some four, five or even six-digit numbers and double them in the same way as you did in the second part of part 2 above. Remember to write down all your thinking stages.

MULTIPLICATION AND DIVISION

C4

PARTITIONING WHEN MULTIPLYING

1. These two examples show a method of *thinking* that will help you with the calculations on this sheet.

$76 \times 8 = (70 \times 8) + (6 \times 8) = 560 + 48 = 608$

$57 \times 14 = (57 \times 10) + (50 \times 4) + (7 \times 4) = 570 + 200 + 28 = 798$

Do these sums in the same way as the first example above. Show all your *thinking stages*.

a. $59 \times 7 =$ _____

b. $6 \times 78 =$ _____

c. $85 \times 8 =$ _____

Do these multiplications in the same way as the second example above. Continue to show all your *thinking stages*.

d. $79 \times 17 =$ _____

e. $68 \times 16 =$ _____

f. $96 \times 19 =$ _____

2. As you work out the answers to the following calculations, try to think in the same way as the first example shown at the top of the page.

a.	46m	×	9	=	**c.**	£58	×	6	=	**e.**	94g	×	7	=
b.	85g	×	7	=	**d.**	67p	×	6	=	**f.**	79m	×	8	=

Now try thinking in the same way as the second example at the top of the page as you tackle these sets of problems.

g.	54m	×	16	=	**i.**	67p	×	19	=	**k.**	£79	×	15	=
h.	96g	×	14	=	**j.**	£85	×	17	=	**l.**	48m	×	18	=

3. Study the completed example below and then do the other two calculations in the same way.

$6.8 \times 6 = (6 \times 6) + (0.8 \times 6)$
$= 36 + 4.8 = 40.8$

$9.4 \times 7 =$ _____

_____

$8.7 \times 9 =$ _____

_____

Write out your thinking stages for the calculations in part 2, using the examples at the top of the page to assist you.

QUICK MENTAL MATHS

DIVISION WITH REMAINDERS

1. Complete these division charts. Give the remainder as a whole number and a fraction in its lowest terms.

÷	101	130	155	170
4	25			
r	1			
r	$\frac{1}{4}$			
6		21		
r		4		
r		$\frac{2}{3}$		
8				21
r				2
r				$\frac{1}{4}$

÷	104	121	163	187
5				37
r				2
r				$\frac{2}{5}$
7			23	
r			2	
r			$\frac{2}{7}$	
9	11			
r	5			
r	$\frac{5}{9}$			

2. Give the answers to the calculations in the same way as the first one has been done.

a. 2086 ÷ 4 | 521 | r | 2 | or | 521.5 |

b. 4263 ÷ 6 | | r | | or | |

c. 2847 ÷ 4 | | r | | or | |

d. 5508 ÷ 5 | | r | | or | |

e. 4793 ÷ 10 | | r | | or | |

f. 7205 ÷ 8 | | r | | or | |

g. 3491 ÷ 100 | | r | | or | |

h. 6054 ÷ 5 | | r | | or | |

3. Read these questions carefully and then fill in the answers.

a. There are 350 people in a theatre audience. How many groups of 47 people can be assembled? _____ How many people will be left over? _____

b. If two hundred and nineteen library books are arranged 30 to the shelf how many shelves will be needed? _____ One shelf would be _____ books less than full.

c. Divide 43,009 by one thousand and give your answer as a decimal fraction. _____

d. Share 7050 by one hundred and show your answer as a mixed fraction. _____

Think of a number. Divide it by 7. If the remainder is 4, what could the number be? Make up a quiz with questions similar to this one. Test your friends and get them to test you.

CALCULATION PATTERNS (× AND ÷)

1. Work out the sequence of rules used in these number patterns.
The completed example gives you the clue!

	A	B	C	D	E	F	G	H	I	J
a.	15	150	30	300	60	600	120	1200	240	2400
b.	25					1000				4000
c.	35			700						5600
d.	45							3600		7200
e.	55		110							8800

2. Write down three statements about the relationship between the patterns of numbers in rows a-e and columns A-J. Make sure your answers are written in complete sentences and are clearly expressed!

a. _____

_____

b. _____

_____

c. _____

_____

3. Keep dividing by 5 until you reach the last amount in each row.
The first row has been completed for you.

a.	£400 000	£80 000	£16 000	£3200	£640	£128
b.	£700 000					£224
c.	£600 000					£192
d.	£900 000					£288

Try and make up some number patterns that help to show the relationship between multiplication and division. Ask your teacher if you can look at sheet C3. It might give you some ideas.

P

QUICK MENTAL MATHS

FACTORS AND MULTIPLYING BY 10, 100, 1000

1. Write down as many pairs of factors as you can find for each of these numbers.

a. 172 _____   168 _____

_____

170 _____

_____

144 _____

150 _____

_____

_____

192 _____   180 _____

_____

b. Write down in words six three-digit numbers that only have themselves and 1 as factors.

_____

_____

2. These examples show you methods of using factors to help you with multiplication and division.

$$34 \times 18 = 34 \times 3 \times 6 = 102 \times 6 = 612 \quad 456 \div 24 = 456 \div 4 \div 6 = 114 \div 6 = 19$$

Do these calculations and write out all the *helping* stages in the same way as the examples above.

a.	32 × 12		**e.**	414 ÷ 18	
b.	27 × 14		**f.**	432 ÷ 16	
c.	35 × 18		**g.**	504 ÷ 24	
d.	34 × 16		**h.**	384 ÷ 12	

3. Think carefully before answering these questions.

a. How many times larger than £564.59 is £56,459? _____

b. How many times larger is four thousand seven hundred than 47? _____

c. How many times smaller than 758g is 0.758g? _____

Make a factor list for other numbers between 100 and 200 in the same way as you did in part 1. If you have time, try to find out which number in this range has the most factors.

NAME _____   CLASS _____

DIVIDING BY 10, 100, 1000

1. Divide each of these numbers by 10, 100 and 1000 and record them on the chart where indicated.

	Millions	Hundred thousands	Ten thousands	Thousands	Hundreds	Tens	Ones	•	Tenths	Hundredths	Thousandths
a.	6	0	9	5	0	1	7	•	0	0	0
÷ 10								•			
÷ 100								•			
÷ 1000								•			
b.	0	2	8	4	0	0	0	•	0	0	0
÷ 10								•			
÷ 100								•			
÷ 1000								•			
c.	5	9	1	8	2	0	7	•	0	0	0
÷ 10								•			
÷ 100								•			
÷ 1000								•			

2. Work out these mm lengths and then change the answers first into cm and then into metres.

a.   14 700mm ÷ 7 = _____ mm   **b.**   63 900mm ÷ 9 = _____ mm

or _____ cm or _____ m   or _____ cm or _____ m

3. Solve these money problems.

a.   Find $\frac{1}{10}$ of £426.90 and give the answer in words. _____

b.   How many times less than £3726 is thirty-seven pounds, twenty-six pence? _____

c.   Make £95 380 a thousand times smaller. _____

 Draw an outline chart like the one in part 1. Replace 10, 100 and 1000 with three numbers of your own and carry out the same instructions.

MULTIPLICATION AND DIVISION

USING RELATED × AND ÷ FACTS

1. More difficult problems can be made easier by doubling one number in the calculation and halving the result. Look at this example: 24 × 15   24 × 30 = 720   720 ÷ 2 = 360.

Finish off these multiplications by writing them out in the same way as the example above.

a. 23 × 15 _____   **d.** 19 × 25 _____

b. 35 × 14 _____   **e.** 46 × 50 _____

c. 73 × 25 _____   **f.** 35 × 21 _____

2. Another way to do difficult calculations is to halve one number and then double the answer. Like this: 20 × 135   10 × 135 = 1350   1350 × 2 = 2700. Now do these sums by writing them out in the same way as the example given.

a. 125 × 14 _____   **d.** 121 × 16 _____

b. 120 × 16 _____   **e.** 225 × 18 _____

c. 115 × 12 _____   **f.** 215 × 14 _____

3. Here are some more ways of using division to help with multiplication. To multiply by 15, multiply by 10, halve the result, then add the two parts together. Try it with these sums.

a. 25 × 15 _____   15 × 15 _____   22 × 15 _____   35 × 15 _____

To multiply by 50, multiply by 100 and halve the result. Try it with these sums.

b. 326 × 50 _____   485 × 50 _____   568 × 50 _____   744 × 50 _____

To multiply by 25, multiply by 100 and then divide the result by 4. Try that with these sums.

c. 52 × 25 _____   28 × 25 _____   64 × 25 _____   76 × 25 _____

 Multiply some more double-digit numbers by 15 and 25 using the same strategies as suggested in part 3. Can you work out a similar method for multiplying by 150 and 250? If so, try it out.

PLACE VALUE WHEN MULTIPLYING AND DIVIDING

1. Write the answers to these calculations first in figures and then in words.

a. 6 390 618 ÷ 3 = _____ _____

_____

b. 521 430 × 2 = _____ _____

_____

c. 8 084 432 ÷ 4 = _____ _____

_____

d. 412 303 × 3 = _____ _____

_____

2. Take care when you place the decimal point in the answers to these sums. Remember the rules!

a. £26.49 × 10 = _____

b. 360m ÷ 1000 = _____

c. 0.7 × 0.9g = _____

d. 0.7km ÷ 2 = _____

e. 4.9cm ÷ 7 = _____

f. Work out a hundredth of eight. _____

g. Multiply 572.36 by a hundred. _____

h. Divide sixty-five by a hundred. _____

i. Make 0.85 twice the size. _____

j. Find a tenth of twenty-seven. _____

3. Write the answers in the first column. In the second column, rearrange the answers as indicated on the table.

2 468 460 ÷ 2	1 234 230	Largest
2 446 068 ÷ 2		
2 486 640 ÷ 2		
2 468 604 ÷ 2		
2 464 608 ÷ 2		Smallest

231 302 × 3		Smallest
3 × 231 230		
232 130 × 3		
3 × 213 032		
231 023 × 3		Largest

Write in words the numbers you have placed in the second column in the tables above.

QUICK MENTAL MATHS

×/÷ WHOLE, FRACTIONAL, DECIMAL AND % AMOUNTS

1. Divide these numbers by 8 and then multiply the answer by 6.

a.

120	176	144	168	104	192	128	184	160	152	112	136
		18				16					
				78		96					

Divide these numbers by 9 and multiply the answer by 5.

b.

144	171	207	153	126	189	216	162	198	117	135	180
			17						13		
		115							65		

2. Work out the following fractional amounts. Concentrate – they are not that difficult!

a. $\frac{8}{9}$ of 270 = _____

b. $\frac{5}{8}$ of 480 = _____

c. $\frac{3}{4}$ of 160 = _____

d. $\frac{6}{10}$ of 600 = _____

e. $\frac{3}{7}$ of 560 = _____

f. $\frac{29}{100}$ of 1000 = _____

g. $\frac{4}{9}$ of 630 = _____

h. $\frac{3}{5}$ of 125 = _____

i. $\frac{3}{100}$ of 2000 = _____

j. $\frac{2}{7}$ of 280 = _____

k. $\frac{3}{8}$ of 720 = _____

l. $\frac{4}{5}$ of 150 = _____

3. Divide these amounts by 6 and give your answer as a percentage (%) of 50.

a.

162	27	54%

c.

216		

e.

108		

b.

288		

d.

174		

f.

234		

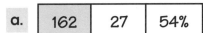 Find 50% of ↓

g. £27.50 × 3 _____

h. 6408kg ÷ 8 _____

i. £20 × 90 _____

Find 25% of ↓

j. 1224kg ÷ 6 _____

k. £25.25 × 8 _____

l. 8240kg ÷ 4 _____

 Find 75% of ↓

m. 7 × £120 _____

n. 4800kg ÷ 8 _____

o. £20 × 50 _____

Make up a price list for ten imaginary items that each cost more than £10.00. Then reduce the total cost of all ten items by the following amounts: 10%, 15%, 20%, 25%, 40%, 60% and 75%.

C13

TEST YOUR SKILLS 1 (C1–C6)

MULTIPLICATION AND DIVISION

C1 Find the product of each pair of numbers.

a. 90, 50 _____   £1.50, 9 _____   7, £1.20 _____   70, 60 _____ ☐

b. 80, 40 _____   8, £1.40 _____   £1.50, 6 _____   80, 50 _____

C2 Divide the smallest number into the largest number in each of these pairs of numbers.

a. 924, 4 _____   10.8, 3 _____   3, 7.35 _____   8, 568 _____ ☐

b. 6, 486 _____   6, 14.4 _____   1.44, 6 _____   357, 7 _____

C3 Write down three other facts using the same numbers as those in each of the facts given.

80 × 15 = 1200	15 × 80 = 1200, 1200 ÷ 15 = 80, 1200 ÷ 80 = 15
2107 ÷ 7 = 301	
9 × 181 = 1629	
1026 ÷ 171 = 6	

☐

C4 Work out:

a. the double of these numbers: eighty _____ 170 _____ 1600 _____

b. the treble of these numbers: ninety _____ 140 _____ 1700 _____

c. four tenths of: 170 _____   1300 _____   35 _____   450 _____   ☐

d. five sevenths of: 126 _____   91 _____ 105 _____   147 _____

C5 Do this problem and write out all the *thinking stages* in the same way as the example below.

67 × 9 = _____

76 × 8 = (70 × 8) + (6 × 8) = 560 + 48 = 608

☐

C6 Answer these two division questions and show the remainders as fractions.

a. Divide nine thousand, six hundred and twenty-three by 6. _____ ☐

b. Five thousand, five hundred and nine shared by 5 equals _____

☐

QUICK MENTAL MATHS

TOTAL

TEST YOUR SKILLS 2 (C7–C12)

C7 Keep dividing by 5 until you reach the last amount in each row.

a.	£100 000	£20 000			£160

b.	£500 000		£20 000		£800

c.	£300 000			£2400	£480

C8 Record as many pairs of factors as you can think of for each of these numbers.

a. 128 _____   136 _____

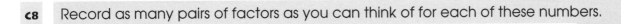

Think carefully before answering these questions.

b. How many times larger than £428.85 is £42 885? _____

c. How many times smaller than 472g is 0.472g? _____

C9 Work out these mm lengths and then change the answers first into cm and then into m.

a. 12 600mm ÷ 6 = _____ mm

or _____ cm or _____ m

b. 48 800mm ÷ 8 = _____ mm

or _____ cm or _____ m

C10 Look at the example below and then complete the calculations in the same way.

24 x 15	24 x 30 = 720	720 ÷ 2 = 360

a. 27 x 15 _____

b. 11 x 35 _____

c. 16 x 25 _____

d. 12 x 45 _____

C11 Make sure you place the decimal point in the correct place in these problems.

a. £32.45 x 10 = _____

b. 240m ÷ 1000 = _____

c. Make 0.65 twice the size. _____

d. How many is a thousandth of 86? _____

C12 Carry out the following operations on the number 600.

a.	b.	c.	d.
÷ 1000	Find 20%	x 100	Find $\frac{3}{4}$

MULTIPLICATION AND DIVISION

C14

TOTAL

THE FOUR RULES OF NUMBER

1. Work out the answers to these calculations. Remember to do any parts in brackets first.

a. $(28p ÷ 7) × 10 = 13p +$ _____

b. $4cm ×$ _____ $= 83cm - 51cm$

c. _____ $= £91 - £14 - £12 + £27$

d. $(240g ÷$ _____$) - (12g + 44g) = 24g$

e. $60ml ÷ 5 = 120ml ÷$ _____

f. $(59km + 21km) + (42km ÷ 6) =$ _____

g. $(83m -$ _____$) + (33m ÷ 3) = 76m$

h. _____ $= (57p + 13p) ÷ (5 × 7)$

i. $7cm × 5 =$ _____ $- 46cm$

j. $(84m + 25m) - (15m + 21m) =$ _____

k. _____ $÷ 4 = 88kg ÷ 11$

l. $24g = (13g × 5) - 14g -$ _____ $- 15g$

2. Study the example that has been done for you. It will help you solve the other problems.

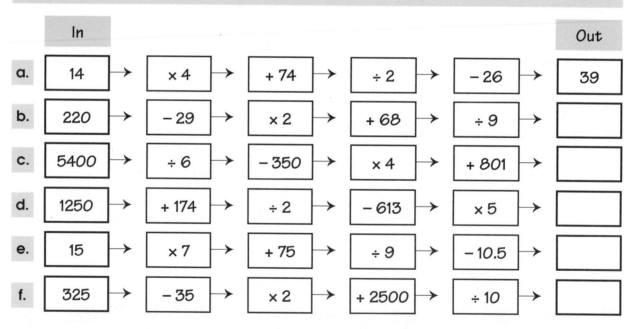

	In					Out
a.	14	× 4	+ 74	÷ 2	− 26	39
b.	220	− 29	× 2	+ 68	÷ 9	
c.	5400	÷ 6	− 350	× 4	+ 801	
d.	1250	+ 174	÷ 2	− 613	× 5	
e.	15	× 7	+ 75	÷ 9	− 10.5	
f.	325	− 35	× 2	+ 2500	÷ 10	

3. Read these problems and then write down the answers.

a. To the product of 1300 and 4 add 6850. _____

b. Find $\frac{5}{8}$ of 640 and subtract one hundred and twenty-six from your answer. _____

Make up some of your own In/Out sums like those in part 2. Don't forget to use all four signs. Try to make up some longer calculations with more operations between the In and the Out numbers.

QUICK MENTAL MATHS

THE FOUR RULES OF NUMBER

1. Work out the answers to these calculations.
Remember to do any parts in brackets first.

a. $81cm - 13cm = 34cm \times$ _____

b. $21p + 14p + 23p -$ _____ $= 47p$

c. _____ $= (9g \times 8) - (2 \times 7g)$

d. $(£63 \div 7) \times (56 \div 4) =$ _____ $+ £26$

e. $360g = (113g - 11g - 12g) \times$ _____

f. $(72km \div 8) \times$ _____ $= 150km - 51km$

g. $900m = (90m \div$ _____ $\div 5) \times 450$

h. _____ $- 22p - 26p + 36p = £1.22$

i. $(51cm + 28cm -$ _____ $\div 2) = 29cm$

j. $£33 + £27 = £79 -$ _____

k. _____ $+ 14m + 16m - 23m = 118m$

l. $(6mm \times 9) + (53mm - 29mm) =$ _____

2. Multiply the two numbers in each left-hand box together, add 1050, halve that answer and then subtract 125. The first one has been done for you.

a.	70, 40	2800	3850	1925	1800
b.	80, 30				
c.	90, 50				
d.	60, 70				
e.	50, 40				
f.	60, 30				

g.	95, 4				
h.	8, 45				
i.	65, 4				
j.	85, 2				
k.	10, 35				
l.	75, 6				

3. Read these problems and work out the answers.

a. To the sum of 3600, 450 and 125 add three hundred and twenty-five. _____

b. From the sum of 2700, 520 and 80 subtract four hundred and eighty-five. _____

c. Find $\frac{1}{12}$ of 720 and multiply your result by ninety. _____

d. Multiply five by ninety-eight and double the answer. _____

e. Work out a third of six hundred and seventy-five shared by three. _____

Choose other pairs of numbers like those in part 2 above. Carry out the same steps.
You could then try a different sequence of instructions.

THE FOUR RULES OF NUMBER

1. Multiply the two numbers together, add 225, divide by 5 and then subtract 21. The first one has been done for you.

a.	45, 3	135	360	72	51

b.	5, 35				

c.	25, 12				

d.	7, 55				

e.	75, 5				

f.	3, 65				

g.	32, 5				

h.	10, 17				

i.	5, 64				

j.	44, 5				

k.	26, 5				

l.	5, 42				

2. Using the +, −, ×, ÷ and = signs make up ten problems that all have at least four different signs in them. Like this: $(46 − 17) + (33 ÷ 3) + (7 × 8) = 96$. The signs can be in any order. You will need to use brackets.

a. _____

b. _____

c. _____

d. _____

e. _____

f. _____

g. _____

h. _____

i. _____

j. _____

3. Solve the problems below. Read each one carefully and think before you start!

A fifth of 855 add seventy-nine is how many? _____

Find the difference between 201 and 351 and multiply your answer by 6. _____

What number is two hundred and fifty more than 45 + 74? _____

Share a half of 500 by ten and then treble the answer. _____

Make six thousand, three hundred $\frac{1}{7}$ the size and divide the result by 4. _____

Using the +, −, ×, ÷ and = signs make up ten more number sentences with brackets like the ones that you did in part 2.

QUICK MENTAL MATHS

MULTISTEP AND MIXED OPERATIONS

D3

THE FOUR RULES OF NUMBER

1. Study the example that has been done for you.
It will help you solve the other problems.

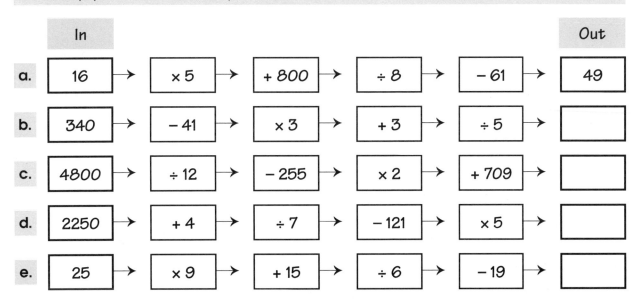

	In					Out
a.	16 →	× 5 →	+ 800 →	÷ 8 →	− 61 →	49
b.	340 →	− 41 →	× 3 →	+ 3 →	÷ 5 →	
c.	4800 →	÷ 12 →	− 255 →	× 2 →	+ 709 →	
d.	2250 →	+ 4 →	÷ 7 →	− 121 →	× 5 →	
e.	25 →	× 9 →	+ 15 →	÷ 6 →	− 19 →	

2. Add the two numbers together, subtract 20, halve that answer and then multiply by 5.

a.	43, 67	110	90	45	225	f.	36, 48			
b.	56, 84					g.	29, 35			
c.	82, 78					h.	59, 17			
d.	69, 81					i.	24, 68			
e.	97, 93					j.	35, 27			

3. Read these questions and work out the answers.

a. Find $\frac{6}{10}$ of 720 and subtract thirty-three from your answer. _____

b. Multiply seven by ninety-nine and find a third of your answer. _____

c. Total up 56, 38, 94 and 62. _____ Subtract this answer from 10 000. _____

d. Share the product of 9 and 8 by the quotient of 24 ÷ 2. _____

 Make up five number problems similar to those in part 3. Each of your problems must involve at least two different mathematical operations. Ask a friend to work out the answers to the questions you have devised.

A1

1. a. **272**, 287, **302**, **317**, 332, 347, 362, 377, 392, **407**
b. **−81ºC**, **−62ºC**, −43ºC, −24ºC, **−5ºC**, 14ºC, 33ºC, 52ºC, **71ºC**, 90ºC
c. 159.27, **159.19**, **159.11**, **159.03**, 158.95, 158.87, 158.79
d. **28 $\frac{5}{7}$**, 28 $\frac{1}{7}$, 27 $\frac{4}{7}$, **27**, **26 $\frac{3}{7}$** , 25 $\frac{6}{7}$, 25 $\frac{2}{7}$, 24 $\frac{5}{7}$, 24 $\frac{1}{7}$,
e. **360**, **350**, **338**, 328, **316**, **306**, 294, 284, 272, 262

2. a. **42 250**, 42 125, 42 000, 41 875, 41 750, 41 625, 41 500, 41 375, **41 250**
b. **1025**, 900, 775, 650, 525, 400, 275, 150, **25**
c. **12 628**, 17 628, 22 628, 27 628, 32 628, 37 628, 42 628, **47 628**
d. **130 307**, 135 307, 140 307, 145 307, 150 307, 155 307, **160 307**

3. a. The following numbers on the square should be shaded:
60, 120, 160, 180, 240, 300, 260, 420, 480
b. five hundred and forty; six hundred
c. 60, 120, 180, 240, 300, 360, 420, 480
d. All of the numbers in the number square.

A2

1. a. 601 b. 4009 c. 20 603 d. 1 626 491 e. 407 107 f. 26 300
g. 300 000 h. 4900 i. 2 407 583 j. 53 724 k. 80 005 l. 610
m. 80 500 n. 20 630 o. 4090

2. a. three thousand and twenty b. eight thousand, two hundred
c. five thousand and two d. twenty-seven thousand, five
hundred and six e. seven hundred and eight thousand and
ninety f. four million, seven hundred and eighty thousand, nine
hundred and nine g. 1275 h. 40 089 i. 269 700

3. a. 0.03 b. 0.05 c. 0.012 d. 0.8 e. 0.2 f. 0.23 g. 0.2 h. 0.4

A3

1. Accept amounts between the following numbers:
a. 100 000 and 106 327, 106 329 and 342 056,
342 058 and above b. 720 489 only, 720 487 and 635 732,
635 730 and below c. 500 001 and 749 999, 750 001 and
999 998, 1 000 000 and above

2. a. < b. > c. < d. = e. < f. > g. > h. < i. > j. = k. < l. < m. >
n. < o. < p. = q. < r. = s. >

3. Open-ended – but the answer fraction must have a different
denominator than the fraction shown here:
a. any fraction less than $\frac{3}{7}$ b. any fraction equal to $\frac{8}{16}$
c. any fraction more than $\frac{5}{9}$ d. any fraction equal to $\frac{15}{20}$
Open-ended – but the answer must be a decimal fraction to
either 2 or 3 decimal places: e. less than 8 f. more than 2.3
g. more than 126.27cm h. less than 91.098km i. less than
3570.4kg j. more than £76.55 k. less than 60.001g l. 50%
m. 2 eighths

A4

1. a. 960, 950 b. 200, 210 c. £546, 550 d. 430, 400
e. 0.073, 0.075 f. 1011, 1000 g. 0.73m, 0.75 h. 520, 500
i. 0.48g, 0.5 j. 740, 750 k. £3.90, 4 l. 4.8, 5

2. a. 9875, 9750, 9625, 9500, 9375, 9250, 9125
b. −200, −50, 100, 300, 450

3. The following values should be circled:
a. $\frac{1}{2}$ and 0.49 b. $\frac{7}{16}$ and $\frac{3}{8}$ c. 0.04 and $\frac{3}{100}$
d. $\frac{3}{4}$ and 74% e. $\frac{3}{9}$ and 33% f. 71% and $\frac{7}{10}$

A5

1. a. £4300, £36 700, £843 000, £900
b. 1000km, 3000km, 9000km, 484 000km
c. 50 000 miles, 460 000 miles, 790 000 miles, 850 000 miles
d. 85cm, 38cm, 444cm, 790cm

2. a. £11.20, £11 b. £1.09, £1 c. £4.09, £4 d. £29.77, £30
e. £2.99, £3 f. £9.60, £10 g. £9.40, £9 h. £1.26, £1
i. £24.80, £25 j. £5.50, £6 k. £5.45, £5 l. £24.50, £25

3. a. 4, 17, 72 b. 10, 58, 845 c. 3, 25, 925 d. 8, 43, 37
e. 3, 37, 46 f. 2.4, 57.4 g. 6.9, 34.9 h. 3.6, 73.5 i. 5.2, 42.4
j. 4, 85.3

A6

A1. a. 260, 170, 80, **− 10**, − 100, − 190, **− 280**, **− 370**
b. **570**, **585**, **595**, 610, **620**, **635**, 645, 660
c. 239.76, 239.83, **239.90**, **239.97**, 240.04, **240.11**
d. **63 $\frac{5}{9}$**, 63, **62 $\frac{4}{9}$**, 61 $\frac{8}{9}$, **61 $\frac{3}{9}$**, 60 $\frac{7}{9}$, **60 $\frac{2}{9}$**
e. 86ºC, **67ºC**, 48ºC, 29ºC, 10ºC, − 9ºC, **− 28ºC**, **−47ºC**
f. **489**, 474, 444, **429**, **414**, 399, 384

A2. a. 3 492 758 b. 32 683 hundreds, 5097 thousands, 509 704 tens
c. 402 d. 6051 e. 30 708 f. 80 000 g. 936 415 h. 10 500 020

A3. a. 2 $\frac{1}{8}$, 2 $\frac{3}{16}$, 2 $\frac{4}{16}$, 2 $\frac{5}{16}$, 2 $\frac{3}{8}$ (other answers possible)
b. **50.02**, 50.01, **50**, 49.99, **49.98** (other answers possible)
c. any number up to 30 000, **30 000**, 30 001, **30 002**, any
number above 30 002
d. **300 001**, 300 000, 299 999, 299 998, **299 997**

A7

A4. a. 580, 600 b. 0.63g, 0.6 c. £477, 500 d. 0.72m, 0.7
e. 5.6, 6 f. 1990, 2000 g. 210, 200 h. £12.60, 12.50
i. 2052, 2050 j. 322p, 325
k. **10 130**, 10 260, 10 390, 10 520, 10 650, 10 780
l. −100, 50, 200, 350

A5. a. 79cm, 50cm, 326cm b. £7900, £252 000, £54 500
c. 1000kg, 4400kg, 91 000kg d. 60 000km, 10 000km, 380 000km
e. 6, 85 f. 8.8, 5.4

B1

1. **a.** 540cm **b.** 825km **c.** 840ml **d.** 17 100g **e.** 45cm **f.** 680kg
   g. 1180mm **h.** 46 min **i.** 740km **j.** £14 100 **k.** 760m **l.** 375cm

2. Open-ended – but the answers should show two, two-digit multiples of 5 or 10 that add up to the following amounts:
   a. 130 **b.** 135 **c.** 120 **d.** 175 **e.** 140 **f.** 145 **g.** 155 **h.** 180 **i.** 185
   j. 150 **k.** 115 **l.** 160
   Open-ended – but the answers should show two, two-digit non-multiples of 5 or 10 that add up to the following amounts and written in words: **m.** 117 **n.** 182 **o.** 163

3. **a.** 81cm **b.** 9840 **c.** 430 **d.** 9.4kg

+	4300	8400
1500	5800	**9900**
5900	10 200	14 300
6800	**11 100**	15 200
3200	7500	11 600
9600	13 900	18 000
7700	12 000	**16 100**

B2

1. **a.** 7.038 **b.** 10.369 **c.** 12.536 **d.** 3.753 **e.** 0.522 **f.** 8.848
   g. 2.165 **h.** 5.419 **i.** 9.614 **j.** 15.508 **k.** 13.354 **l.** 4.607
   Open-ended – but each answer should show a two-digit number subtracted from a three-digit number and giving the answers indicated: **m.** seventy-three **n.** sixty-eight **o.** fifty-seven **p.** forty-five

2. **a.** 49cm **b.** 13 500cm **c.** $23\frac{1}{2}$ kg **d.** £3840 **e.** 156ml **f.** 21 500
   g. 440km **h.** 16 000 **i.** 275cm **j.** 470kg **k.** 39hrs **l.** 3805m

3.
–	3173	5284
630	2543	**4654**
820	2353	4464
570	**2603**	4714
750	2423	4534
420	2753	4864
940	2233	**4344**

   b. 0.35 **c.** £4.77 **d.** 111km **e.** 736 000

B3

1. **a.** (completed example - sums in any order)
   b. 731, 475 + 256, 731 – 475, 731 – 256
   c. 9500, 1700 + 7800, 9500 – 7800, 9500 – 1700
   d. 2760, 4060 – 2760, 1300 + 2760, 2760 + 1300
   e. 5801, 5472 + 329, 5801 – 329, 5801 – 329, 5801 – 5472

2. (4819, 4170, 649) (6913, 423, 6490) (3950, 370, 3580) (7706, 356, 7350)
   4170 + 649 = 4819, 4819 – 4170 = 649, 4819 – 649 = 4170
   423 + 6490 = 6913, 6913 – 423 = 6490, 6913 – 6490 = 423
   370 + 3580 = 3950, 3950 – 370 = 3580, 3950 – 3580 = 370
   356 + 7350 = 7706, 7706 – 356 = 7350, 7706 – 7350 = 356

3. **a.** These addition facts with numbers in any order:
   2730 + 189 = 2919
   5660 + 290 = 5950
   8250 + 574 = 8824
   9830 + 172 = 10 002
   b. Subtraction facts using the three numbers given:
   5007, 860, 4147
   8030, 2800, 5230
   7450, 390, 7060
   6680, 880, 5800

B4

1. **a.** 520, 470, 340, 260, 130, 350
   b. 318, 126, 207, 333, 476, 555
   c. 1267, 1775, 1010, 880, 1614
   d. 710, 1959, 1652, 1388, 339

2. **a.** one hundred and sixty thousand **b.** twenty-seven thousand
   c. sixty-four thousand **d.** five hundred and eighty thousand, five hundred and sixty-four **e.** fifty-six thousand, nine hundred and ninety-nine

3.
560	1120	2240	660	1320	2640	380	760	1520
750	1500	3000	890	1780	3560	870	1740	3480
970	1940	3880	470	940	1880	740	1480	2960

B5

1. **a.** 1337 **b.** 2888 **c.** 9321 **d.** 8716 **e.** 4113 **f.** 6695
   g. 2326kg **h.** 5459ml **i.** £11 142 **j.** 7050ml **k.** £6200
   l. 8510m

2. **a.** £10.00 **b.** 6672 **c.** 1006 110 **d.** open-ended – one sum of four digits with each figure having a different number of digits

3. Open-ended – ten addition sums each with three numbers using all the numbers given (check that the largest number is first in each sum).

B6

1. **a.** 11 850m **b.** 8550km **c.** £15 050 **d.** 17 750g **e.** 10 250kg
   f. £6225

2. **a.** 25 000 + 25 000 – 300 = 50 000 – 300 = 49 700
   b. 38 000 + 38 000 – 1000 = 75 000
   or 37 000 + 37 000 + 1000 = 75 000
   c. 47 000 + 47 000 – 200 – 100 = 93 700

3. **a.** 23 100 **b.** 26 550 **c.** 20 450 **d.** 9900

B7

1.
135	156	177	198	219
154	**175**	196	217	238
173	194	**215**	236	257
192	213	234	**255**	276
211	232	253	274	**295**

999	968	937	906	**875**
970	939	908	**877**	846
941	910	**879**	848	817
912	**881**	850	819	788
883	852	821	790	759

2.
755	**1205**	**1960**	8700	**2400**	11,100
245	2005	**2250**	3620	**4900**	**8520**
1000	**3210**	4210	**12 320**	7300	19 620

3.
–	7100	8200	9300
2600	4500	5600	6700
3700	3400	**4500**	5600
4800	2300	**3400**	4500
5900	1200	2300	3400

–	624	734	844
150	**474**	584	694
260	364	**474**	584
370	254	**364**	474
480	144	254	**364**

B8

1. **a.** 500 + 200 + 30 + 80 + 7 + 4 = 700 + 110 + 11 = 821
   b. 100 + 600 + 60 + 40 + 8 + 2 = 700 + 100 + 10 = 810
   c. 386 + 14 + 533 = 400 + 533 = 933
   d. 844 **e.** 999 **f.** 927

2.
969	+	557		
= 900	+	500		
+ 60	+	50		
+ 9	+	7		
= 1400	+	110	+	16
= 1526				

745	+	865		
= 700	+	800		
+ 40	+	60		
+ 5	+	5		
= 1500	+	100	+	10
= 1610				

3. **a.** 860 **b.** 1616

B9

1. a. 638m + 500m − 21m = 1138m − 21m = 1117m
b. 914kg − 600kg + 13kg = 314kg + 13kg = 327kg
c. £4523 − £3000 + £209 = £1523 + £209 = £1732
d. 3746km + 9000km − 27km = 12 746km − 27km = 12 719km

2. a. 6493 − 2000 − 300 − 60 − 7 = 4493 − 300 − 60 − 7
= 4193 − 60 − 7 = 4133 − 7 = 4126
b. 3386 + 900 + 500 + 20 + 7 = 12386 + 500 + 20 + 7 = 12 913
(Could also include 12 886 + 20 + 7 = 12 906 + 7 = 12 913)

3. a. £5276 b. 17.44m (17m 44cm)

B10

1. a. 12m b. 39km c. £2265 d. 650kg e. £7.68 f. 155
g. six hundred and fifty thousand h. 399ml i. 4886km
j. 800cm k. 49hrs

2. Accept top-heavy and mixed fraction answers
a. $3+4 = \frac{7}{12}$ b. $8+7 = \frac{15}{10}$ c. $4-3 = \frac{1}{8}$
d. $5-3 = \frac{2}{10}$ e. $8+5 = \frac{13}{10}$ f. $7+9 = \frac{16}{12}$
g. $5-2 = \frac{3}{8}$ h. $7-6 = \frac{1}{10}$

3.

+	68p	97p	69p	58p	76p	66p	49p	57p	86p	47p	78p
£5.75	£6.43	£6.72	£6.44	£6.33	£6.51	£6.41	£6.24	£6.32	£6.61	£6.22	£6.53

−	96cm	32cm	55cm	64cm	48cm	62cm	41cm	33cm	57cm	81cm	79cm
4.8m	3.84m	4.48m	4.25m	4.16m	4.32m	4.18m	4.39m	4.47m	4.23m	3.99m	4.01m

B11

1. a. thirty thousand, two hundred b. eighteen thousand, nine hundred c. three hundred and eight thousand, eight hundred d. four hundred and twenty-six thousand, seven hundred and five e. eleven million, three hundred and thirty

2. a. 3.82, 8 tenths ($\frac{8}{10}$) b. 14.58, 8 hundredths ($\frac{8}{100}$)
c. 4800, 8 hundreds d. 8250, 8 thousands e. 98, 8 units
f. 0.278, 8 thousandths ($\frac{8}{1000}$)

3.

1050 500	1 505 005
1 505 005	1 055 055
1 005 050	1 050 500
1 055 055	1 050 050
1 050 050	1 005 050

404 404	404 044
440 004	404 404
440 400	404 440
404 440	440 004
404 044	440 400

B12

1. a. 77cm b. 34ml c. 38km d. 54kg e. £93.00 f. 1820mm
g. £450.00 h. 620kg

2.

−	1610	1650	1910	1750	1520	1510	1720	1830	1840	1540	1630
160	1450		1750	1590	1360		1560	1670	1680	1380	1470
170	1440	1480			1350	1340		1660			1460
190		1460	1720	1560		1320	1530		1650	1350	
	10	20	30	30	10	20	30	10	30	30	10

3. The following number combinations should be found in each shape – reading from left to right/top to bottom:
a. 5, 25, 25, 25, 20 b. 10, 5, 25, 25, 20, 15 c. 10, 5, 15, 5, 25, 25, 15 d. 20, 15, 20, 15, 30 e. 20, 20, 10, 20, 30 f. 15, 5, 25, 20, 15, 20 g. 5, 25, 20, 20, 30 h. 20, 30, 5, 15, 5, 25 i. 15, 5, 25, 20, 15, 20 j. 20, 10, 15, 30, 25 k. 15, 30, 5, 25, 25

B13

B1. a. 190, 540, 5200 b. 105, 1058, 7983 c. 155, 605, 4929
d. 119, 579, 9700

B2. a. 1 629 000 b. 4705km

B3. The following four facts in any order:
a. 2003 + 898 = 2901, 898 + 2003 = 2901, 2901 − 2003 = 898,
2901 − 898 = 2003,
b. 5650 + 2390 = 8040, 2390 + 5650 = 8040, 8040 − 5650 = 2390,
8040 − 2390 = 5650

B4.

470	940	1880	550	1100	2200	680	1360	2720
730	1460	2920	990	1980	3960	860	1720	3440

B5. Open-ended – four addition sums each with three numbers using all the amounts given (largest number first)

B6. (£4000 + £4000) − £300 − £100 = £7600

B14

B7.

1320	4750	6070	480	1320	1800
450	540	990	1860	370	2230
1770	5290	7060	2340	1690	4030

−	7120	7230	7340	8450	8560	8670
2505	4615	4725	4835	5945	6055	6165

B8. a. 437 + 568 = 400 + 500 + 30 + 60 + 7 + 8 = 900 + 90 + 15 = 1005 b. 486 + 257 = 486 + 14 + 243 = 500 + 243 = 743

B9. a. 283m + 588m = 283m + 600m − 12m = 883m − 12m = 871m
b. 837g − 589g = 837g − 600g + 11g = 237g + 11g = 248g

B10. a. $\frac{10+6}{15} = \frac{16}{15}$ or $1\frac{1}{15}$ b. $\frac{6-3}{8} = \frac{3}{8}$ c. 38 d. £6.13
e. 4.91cm (4m 91cm, 491cm)

B11. a. 5.02, 2 hundredths ($\frac{2}{100}$) b. 12.45, 2 units

B12. 90

C1

1. a. 20cm b. 9km c. 320ml d. 50 e. 40 ltrs f. 30kg
g. 180mm h. 6 i. 6km j. 60cm k. £700 l. 50m

2. a. 2800 b. 4500 c. 6400 d. 1800 e. 2400 f. 4200 g. 3500 h. 3200
i. 2500 j. 600 k. 1800 l. 4000

£8.40	£10.50	£9.80	£9.10
£6.00	£7.50	£7.00	£6.50
£10.80	£13.50	£12.60	£11.70
£9.60	£12.00	£11.20	£10.40
£7.20	£9.00	£8.40	£7.80

3. a. 7350 cups b. 720ml c. 1260 d. 0.42

C2

1. a. 61, 91, 71 b. 181, 101, 51 c. 181, 171, 201
d. 191, 231, 51 e. 191, 71, 161 f. 51, 131, 41

÷	6400	10 400	13 600	16 800
20	320	520	680	840
40	160	260	340	420
80	80	130	170	210
÷	1080	1350	1620	1890
90	12	15	18	21

2. a. 20g b. 8 c. 720m d. 7 e. 70m f. 9 g. 490cm h. 5 i. 80 min j. 7
k. 360kg l. 9

3. a. 21 b. 1.4 c. 12.5 d. 13 e. £3.90

÷	10.8	14.4	13.2
3	3.6	4.8	4.4
6	1.8	2.4	2.2
12	0.9	1.2	1.1
÷	1.08	1.44	1.32
3	0.36	0.48	0.44
6	0.18	0.24	0.22

C3

1. a. (completed example - sums in any order)
b. 1050, 70 × 15 = 1050, 1050 ÷ 70 = 15, 1050 ÷ 15 = 70
c. 1890, 210 × 9 = 1890, 1890 ÷ 210 = 9 1890 ÷ 9 = 210
d. 150, 1350 ÷ 150 = 9, 9 × 150 = 1350, 150 × 9 = 1350
e. 1140, 60 × 19 = 1140, 1140 ÷ 60 = 19, 1140 ÷ 19 = 60

2. (19, 7, 133) (23, 6, 138) (19, 171, 9) (23, 115, 5)
133 ÷ 7 = 19, 7 × 19 = 133, 19 × 7 = 133
138 ÷ 6 = 23, 6 × 23 = 138, 23 × 6 = 138
171 ÷ 9 = 19, 9 × 19 = 171, 19 × 9 = 171
115 ÷ 5 = 23, 5 × 23 = 115, 23 × 5 = 115

3. a. 1848 ÷ 8 = 231, 1848 ÷ 231 = 8
1190 ÷ 7 = 170, 1190 ÷ 170 = 7
1446 ÷ 6 = 241, 1446 ÷ 241 = 6
b. 181 × 9 = 1629, 9 × 181 = 1629
190 × 8 = 1520, 8 × 190 = 1520
171 × 6 = 1026, 6 × 171 = 1026

C4

1. a. 32cm, 8400kg, 44km b. 1200ml, £540.00, 1890mm
c. 69, 55, 91, 39

2. a. 200 + 140 + 14 = 354
b. 600 + 160 + 2 = 762
c. 800 + 160 + 12 = 972
d. 400 + 140 + 18 = 558

3. a. 42, 15, 210, 31.2, 618
b. 63, 72, 570, 51, 6900
c. 45, 55, 90, 20, 3500

d. $\frac{9}{20}$ e. $\frac{7}{25}$ f. $\frac{1}{4}$ g. 0.6 h. $\frac{1}{8}$ i. 0.56

C5

1. a. (50 × 7) + (9 × 7) = 350 + 63 = 413
b. (6 × 70) + (6 × 8) = 420 + 48 = 468
c. (80 × 8) + (5 × 8) = 640 + 40 = 680
d. (79 × 10) + (70 × 7) + (9 × 7) = 790 + 490 + 63 = 1343
e. (68 × 10) + (60 × 6) + (8 × 6) = 680 + 360 + 48 = 1088
f. (96 × 10) + (90 × 9) + (6 × 9) = 960 + 810 + 54 = 1824

2. a. 414m b. 595g c. £348 d. 402p e. 658g f. 632m g. 864m
h. 1344g i. 1273g j. £1445 k. £1185 l. 864m

3. (9 × 7) + (0.4 × 7) = 63 + 2.8 = 65.8
(8 × 9) + (0.7 × 9) = 72 + 6.3 = 78.3

C6

1.

	101	130	155	170
4	**25**	32	38	42
r	**1**	2	3	2
r	$\frac{1}{4}$	$\frac{1}{2}$	$\frac{3}{4}$	$\frac{1}{2}$
6	16	**21**	25	28
r	5	**4**	5	2
r	$\frac{5}{6}$	$\frac{2}{3}$	$\frac{5}{6}$	$\frac{1}{3}$
8	12	16	19	**21**
r	5	2	3	**2**
r	$\frac{5}{8}$	$\frac{1}{4}$	$\frac{3}{8}$	$\frac{1}{4}$

	104	121	163	187
5	20	24	32	**37**
r	4	1	3	**2**
r	$\frac{4}{5}$	$\frac{1}{5}$	$\frac{3}{5}$	$\frac{2}{5}$
7	14	17	**23**	26
r	6	2	**2**	5
r	$\frac{6}{7}$	$\frac{2}{7}$	$\frac{2}{7}$	$\frac{5}{7}$
9	**11**	13	18	20
r	**5**	4	1	7
r	$\frac{5}{9}$	$\frac{4}{9}$	$\frac{1}{9}$	$\frac{7}{9}$

2. a. completed example b. 710 r 3 or 710.5 c. 711 r 3 or 711.75
d. 1101 r 3 or 1101.6 e. 479 r 3 or 479.3 f. 900 r 5 or 900.625
g. 34 r 91 or 34.91 h. 1210 r 4 or 1210.8

3. a. 7, 21 b. 8, 21 c. 43.009 d. 70 $\frac{1}{2}$

C7

1. a. completed example
b. 25, 250, 50, 500, 100, **1000**, 200, 2000, 400, **4000**
c. 35, 350, 70, **700**, 140, 1400, 280, 2800, 560, **5600**
d. 45, 450, 90, 900, 180, 1800, 360, **3600**, 720, **7200**
e. 55, 550, **110**, 1100, 220, 2200, 440, 4400, 880, **8800**

2. a–c. Open-ended – accept any three relevant answers in complete sentences.

3. a. £80 000, £16 000, £3200, £640
b. £140 000, £28 000, £5600, £1120
c. £120 000, £24 000, £4800, £960
d. £180 000, £36 000, £7200, £1440

C8

1. a. 172 – (1, 172) (2, 86) (4, 43)
170 – (1, 170) (2, 85) (5, 34) (10, 17)
150 – (1, 150) (2, 75) (3, 50) (6, 25) (10, 15)
192 – (1, 192) (2, 96) (3,64) (4, 48) (6, 32) (8, 24) (12, 16)
168 – (1, 168) (2, 84) (3, 56) (4, 42) (6, 28) (7, 24) (8, 21) (12, 14)
144 – (1, 144) (2, 72) (3, 48) (4, 36) (6,24) (8, 18) (9, 16) (12, 12)
180 – (1, 180) (2, 90) (3, 60) (4, 45) (5, 36) (9, 20) (10, 18) (12,15)
b. Open-ended – six numbers written in words with only 1 and themselves as factors.

2. a. 32 × 3 × 4 = 96 × 4 = 384 b. 27 × 2 × 7 = 54 × 7 = 378
c. 35 × 2 × 9 = 70 × 9 = 630 d. 34 × 4 × 4 = 136 × 4 = 544
e. 414 ÷ 3 ÷ 6 = 138 ÷ 6 = 23 f. 432 ÷ 4 ÷ 4 = 108 ÷ 4 = 27
g. 504 ÷ 4 ÷ 6 = 126 ÷ 6 = 21 h. 384 ÷ 3 ÷ 4 = 128 ÷ 4 = 32

3. a. 100 b. 100 c. 1000

C9

1. a. ÷ 10 = 609 501.7
÷ 100 = 60 950.17
÷ 1000 = 6095.017
b. ÷ 10 = 28 400
÷ 100 = 2840
÷ 1000 = 284
c. ÷ 10 = 591 820.7
÷ 100 = 59 182.07
÷ 1000 = 5918.207

2. a. 2100mm or 210cm or 2.1m b. 7100mm or 710cm or 7.1m

3. a. forty-two pounds sixty-nine pence b. 100 times less c. £95.38

C10

1. a. 23 × 15, 23 × 30 = 690, 690 ÷ 2 = 345
b. 35 × 14, 70 × 14 = 980, 980 ÷ 2 = 490
c. 73 × 25, 73 × 50 = 3650, 3650 ÷ 2 = 1825
d. 19 × 25, 19 × 50 = 950, 950 ÷ 2 = 475
e. 46 × 50, 46 × 100 = 4600, 4600 ÷ 2 = 2300
f. 35 × 21, 70 × 21 = 1470, 1470 ÷ 2 = 735

2. a. 125 × 14, 125 × 7 = 875, 875 × 2 = 1750
b. 120 × 16, 120 × 8 = 960, 960 × 2 = 1920
c. 115 × 12, 115 × 6 = 690, 690 × 2 = 1380
d. 121 × 16, 121 × 8 = 968, 968 × 2 = 1936
e. 225 × 18, 225 × 9 = 2025, 2025 × 2 = 4050
f. 215 × 14, 215 × 7 = 1505, 1505 × 2 = 3010

3. a. 375, 225, 330, 525 b. 16 300, 24 250, 28 400, 37 200 c. 1300, 700, 1600, 1900

C11

1. a. 2130206 two million, one hundred and thirty thousand, two hundred and six b. 1042860 one million, forty-two thousand, eight hundred and sixty c. 2021108 two million, twenty-one thousand, one hundred and eight d. 1236909 one million, two hundred and thirty-six thousand, nine hundred and nine

2. a. £264.90 b. 0.36m c. 0.63g d. 0.35km e. 0.7cm f. 0.08 g. 57236 h. 0.65 i. 1.7 j. 2.7

3.

1234230	1243320
1223034	1234302
1243320	1234230
1234302	1232304
1232304	1223034

693906	639096
693690	693069
696390	693690
639096	693906
693069	696390

C12

1.

120	176	144	168	104	192	128	184	160	152	112	136
15	22	**18**	21	13	24	**16**	23	20	19	14	17
90	132	108	126	**78**	144	**96**	138	120	114	84	102

144	171	207	153	126	189	216	162	198	117	135	180
16	19	23	**17**	14	21	24	18	22	**13**	15	20
80	95	**115**	85	70	105	120	90	110	**65**	75	100

2. a. 240 b. 300 c. 120 d. 360 e. 240 f. 290 g. 280 h. 75 i. 60 j. 80 k. 270 l. 120

3. a. **162, 27, 54%** b. 288, 48, 96% c. 216, 36, 72% d. 174, 29, 58% e. 108, 18, 36% f. 234, 39, 78% g. £41.25 h. 400 kg i. £900 j. 51kg k. £50.50 l. 515kg m. £630 n. 450kg o. £750

C13

C1. a. 4500, £13.50, £8.40, 4200 b. 3200, £11.20, £9.00, 4000

C2. a. 231, 3.6, 2.45, 71 b. 81, 2.4, 0.24, 51

C3. a. (completed example)
b. 2107 ÷ 301 = 7, 301 × 7 = 2107, 7 × 301 = 2107
c. 181 × 9 = 1629, 1629 ÷ 9 = 181, 1629 ÷ 181 = 9
d. 1026 ÷ 6 = 171, 6 × 171 = 1026, 171 × 6 = 1026

C4. a. 160, 340, 3200 b. 270, 420, 5100 c. 68, 520, 14, 180 d. 90, 65, 75, 105

C5. 67 × 9 = (60 × 9) + (7 × 9) = 540 + 63 = 603

C6. a. $1603\frac{5}{6}$ b. $1101\frac{4}{5}$

C14

C7. a. **£20 000**, £4000, £800
b. £100 000, **£20 000**, £4000
c. £60 000, £12 000, **£2400**

C8. a. 128 – (1, 128) (2, 64) (4, 32) (8, 16)
136 – (1, 136) (2, 68) (4, 34) (8, 17)
b. 100 c. 1000

C9. a. 2100mm or 210cm or 2.1m b. 6100mm or 610cm or 6.1m

C10. 27 × 15, 27 × 30 = 810, 810 ÷ 2 = 405
11 × 5, 11 × 70 = 770, 770 ÷ 2 - 385
16 × 25, 16 × 50 = 800 800 ÷ 2 = 400
12 × 45, 12 × 90 = 1080, 1080 ÷ 2 = 540

C11. a. £324.50 b. 0.24m c. 1.3 d. 0.086

C12. a. 0.6 b. 120 c. 60 000 d. 450

D1

1. a. 27p b. 8 c. £92 d. 3 e. 10 f. 87km g. 18m h. 2p i. 81cm j. 73m k. 32kg l. 12g

2.

14	39
220	50
5400	3001
1250	495
15	9.5
325	308

3. a. 12050 b. 274

D2

1. a. 2 b. 11p c. 58g d. £100 e. 4 f. 11 g. 9 h. £1.34 i. 21cm j. £19 k. 111m l. 78mm

2. a. **2800, 3850, 1925, 1800** b. 2400, 3450, 1725, 1600 c. 4500, 5550 2775, 2650 e. 4200, 5250, 2625, 2500 e. 2000, 3050, 1525, 1400 f. 1800, 2850, 1425, 1300 g. 380, 1430, 715, 590 h. 360, 1410, 705 580 i. 260, 1310, 655, 530 j. 170, 1220, 610, 485 k. 350, 1400, 700 575 l. 450, 1500, 750, 625

3. a. 4500 b. 2815 c. 5400 d. 980 e. 75

D3

1. a. **135, 360, 72, 51** b. 175, 400, 80, 59 c. 300, 525, 105, 84 d. 385, 610, 122, 101 e. 375, 600, 120, 99 f. 195, 420, 84, 63 g. 160, 385, 77, 56 h. 170, 395, 79, 58 i. 320, 545, 109, 88 j. 220, 445, 89, 68 k. 130, 355, 71, 50 l. 210, 435, 87, 66

2. Open-ended – ten problems all with at least four different signs in them chosen from +, –, ×, ÷ and =.

3. a. 250 b. 900 c. 369 d. 75 e. 225

D4

1.

16	49
340	180
4800	999
2250	1005
25	21

2. a. **110, 90, 45, 225** b. 140, 120, 60, 300 c. 160, 140, 70, 350 d. 150, 130, 65, 325 e. 190, 170, 85, 425 f. 84, 64, 32, 160 g. 64, 44, 22, 110 h. 76, 56, 28, 140 i. 92, 72, 36, 180 j. 62, 42, 21, 105

3. a. 399 b. 231 c. 250, 9750 d. 6